Basic Pneumatic Technology

Bulletin 0248-B1

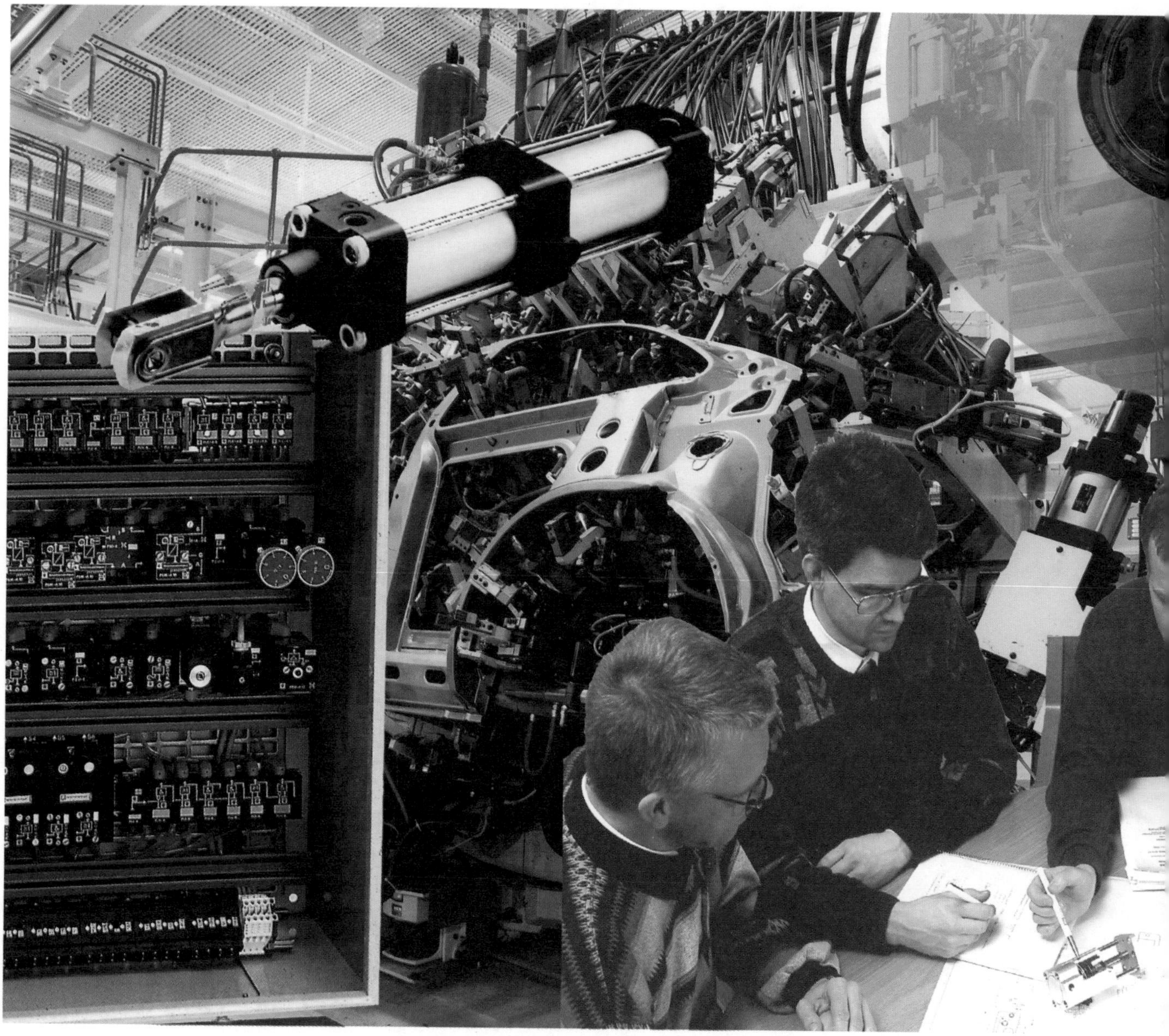

First Printing .... March, 1998
Second Printing .... January, 2001

Printed in The United States of America

Module 1

Introduction to Compressed Air

Contents

Introduction to Compressed Air

Objectives

In this section the following will be examined:

- Significant properties of gases
- Components
- Symbols and Standards
- Safety procedures
- Summary

Gas Laws

The Earth is surrounded by an envelope of air known as the Earth's atmosphere.

The composition of this 12-mile thick envelope is shown opposite.

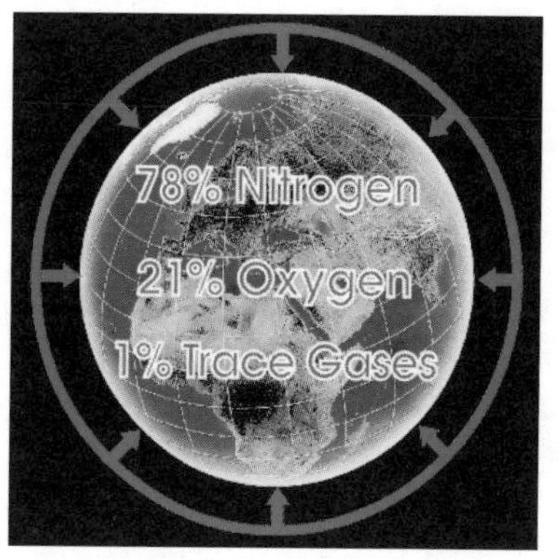

It is this **atmospheric air** that forms the raw material used in industrial pneumatic systems.

Air at ground level is at a certain pressure.

This is because of the large mass of air above it.

That ground level pressure can be expressed as a force per unit area.

$$\text{Pressure} = \frac{\text{Force}}{\text{Area}}$$

In the figure shown, that force is the collision of the air molecules with the surface area of the closed vessel.

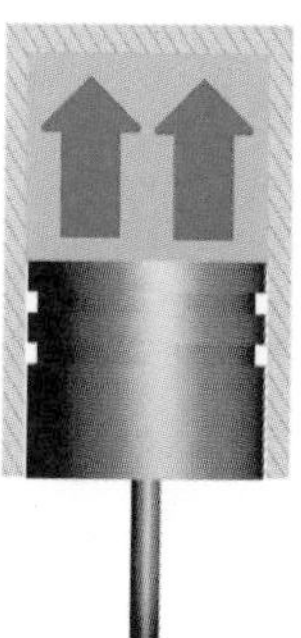

Air confined in this way exerts **equal pressure** on **all** surfaces of the vessel. This is known as **elasticity**.

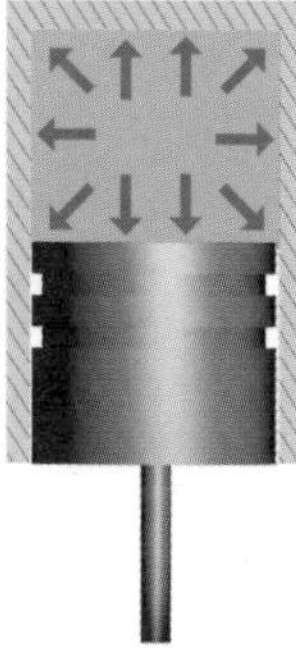

In standard industrial practice pressure is expressed in units of "bar," "pounds per square inch" (psi) or "Pascal" (Pa).

One "bar" is equivalent to 14.5 pounds of force acting on a square inch of a surface or 14.5 psi.

A force of approximately 10 Newtons acting on a surface area of one square centimeter is also the equivalent of 1 bar.

1 bar = 14.5 psi = 10^5Pa = 10N/Cm^2

Air is a compressible substance and, as well as being elastic, it is able to return to its original state or condition after being deformed.

This means that it lends itself to change in volume.

If the volume of the vessel is reduced then the volume of the air inside is also reduced, we say it has been compressed.

This represents a fundamental difference between liquids and gases.

Gases are **compressible**.

Liquids are virtually **non-compressible**.

The force acting on the surface area has increased due to the reduction in volume of the air in the vessel.

This has altered the pressure within the vessel and the air has become compressed.

These changes can be described using the **gas laws**.

The **compressibility** of a gas was first investigated by Robert Boyle in 1662. He discovered that the pressure (P) and the volume (V) of a particular quantity of gas was constant (C), provided that the temperature did not vary.

Boyle's Law holds temperature constant.

Pressure x **V**olume = **C**onstant **P x V = C**

Theoretically by halving the volume of air contained in a vessel, means that its pressure is doubled. Only in this way can the product of **pressure** and **volume** remain **constant**.

Therefore, when we **compress** a gas, we **pressurize** it.

In 1787 J.A.C. Charles, a French physicist, first experimented on the thermal expansion of gases. He found that the **volume** of a gas increased in equal amounts for equal increased increments of **temperature**.

This law was later formalized by Gay Lussac into the form shown below:

$$\text{Volume}_1 = \text{Volume}_2 \times \frac{\text{Temperature}_1}{\text{Temperature}_2}$$

$$V_1 = V_2 \times \frac{T_1}{T_2}$$

or

$$V_2 = V_1 \times \frac{T_2}{T_1}$$

Charles law keeps **pressure constant**.

Gay Lussac concluded that 'At **constant pressure** (P) the **volume** (V) of a gas increases in proportion to the **temperature** (T).'

An alternative form of this law is that 'At constant volume (V) the pressure (P) is proportional to the temperature (T).

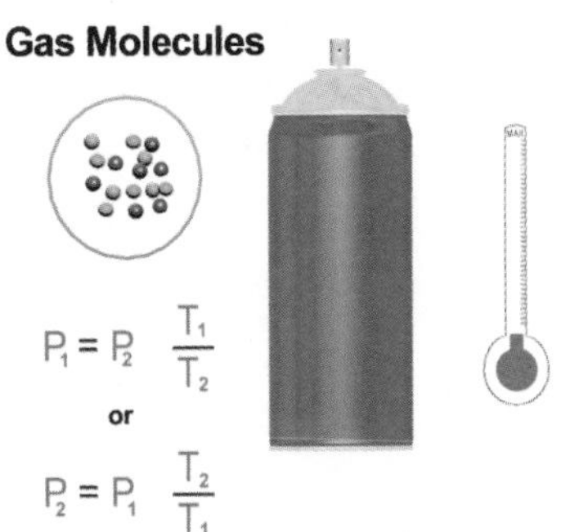

Here we see that the air molecules increase in velocity with an increase in temperature.

This is turn results in an increase in pressure.

If compressed gas in a vessel, such at this aerosol can, is heated the pressure will increase.

SAFETY NOTE: **It is for this reason that empty aerosol cans should never be incinerated or subject to temperatures in excess of those stated by the manufacturer on the can.**

The heat will increase the pressure within the vessel, leading ultimately to an explosion.

If you have ever pumped up a bicycle tire you will have found that the end of the pump gets hot.

This is a consequence of Charles / Gay Lussac's Law. When a gas is compressed, its temperature rises.

Most industrial pneumatic systems use compressed air. Atmospheric air is compressed to generate pressurized air which is used to operate these industrial pneumatic systems.

It is this pressure that provides the driving force for these systems. The pressure gauge is an instrument which measures this pressure.

Most pressure gauges measure the pressure **above** atmospheric. This is known as **relative** or **gauge pressure**. To determine the **absolute pressure** from a gauge reading, **atmospheric pressure** must be added.

Pressure in Bar

Working Pressure Level

P.abs

P.rel

Normal Atmospheric Pressure Level (Variable)

1.013 bar/14.7 psi

P.atm

0

Absolute Vacuum

P.abs = P.atm + P.rel

P.abs. : absolute pressure
P.ref. : relative pressure
P.atm. : atmospheric pressure

The usefulness of using compressed air as a power system is due to one further characteristic.

This is because the pressure in an enclosed fluid power system is transmitted, undiminished, in all directions throughout the system.

This means that force is transmitted, undiminished, in all directions throughout a pneumatic system.

Force (F) = Pressure (P) x Area (A)

Also Pressure (P) = $\frac{\text{Force (F)}}{\text{Area (A)}}$

Area (A) = $\frac{\text{Force (F)}}{\text{Pressure (P)}}$

This was first established by Blaise Pascal, a French mathematician and philosopher.

Example Calculation 1

F = P x A
= 100 psi x 10 in^2
= 1000 lbf

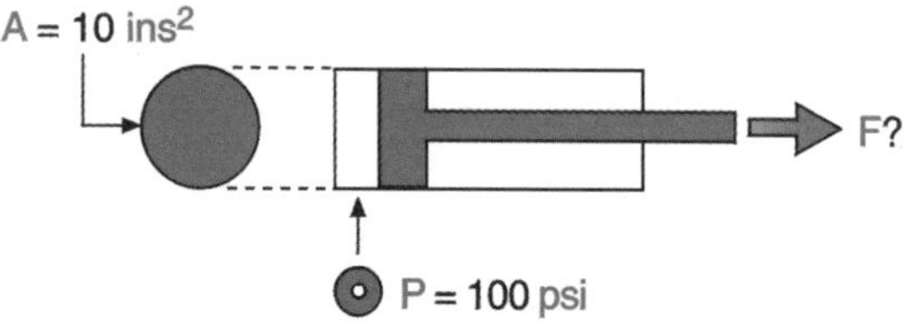

Example Calculations

1. The relationship of these elements, **pressure**, **force** and **area**, is known as **Pascal's Law**. We have a pressure of 100 psi, working on a

piston area of 10in². What would be the resultant **force (F)**?

From Pascal's Law the **Pressure (P)** is multiplied by the **area (A)**, to give the **force (F).**

2. We have a **pressure (P)** of 10 bar acting on a piston **area (A)** of 5 cm².

   What would be the resultant **force (F)**?

   Note that the SI unit for force is the **Newton (N)**; therefore, the pressure in **bar** must be changed to Newtons per Square Centimeter (N/cm²).

   9.81 N/cm² = 1 bar. However, for ease of calculation 10 N/cm² is used.

   To calculate the **area (A)** of a given diameter, one of the calculations shown should be used.

3. What **pressure (P)** would be required to move a **force (F)** of 2000lb if the cylinder piston **area (A)** is 20 in²?

   Again using Pascal's Law we can calculate the equivalent **pressure (P)**.

   However, other factors must be taken into account. 100 psi pressure would result in an equilibrium pressure and not move the load.

   Therefore, a design factor to overcome both the load **force (F)** and friction should be used. This is normally an additional 30%.

The conversion from **pounds** to **Newtons** is

SI Standard - 1 lbf = 4.525 Newtons (N)

Boyle's Law

Example Calculations

Initial pressure (P_1) times the initial volume (V_1) equals the final pressure (P_2) times the final volume (V_2) = a constant (C)
(P1 & P2 in Absolute units).

Example Calculation 2

F = P x A
P = 10 bar x 10N / cm^2
= 100 N / cm^2
A = 5 cm^2
F = 100 N / cm^2 x 5 cm^2
= 500 Newtons

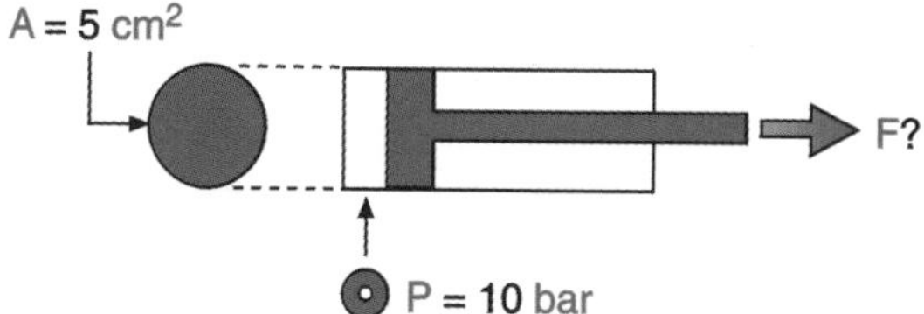

Example Calculation

Area = $\frac{\pi d^2}{4}$ or πr^2

d = Diameter
r = Radius

π = 3.142 or $\frac{22}{7}$

Alternative Area calculation
= d^2 x 0.7854

Example Calculation 3

$P = \frac{F}{A}$

$= \frac{2000 \text{ lb}}{20 \text{ ins}^2}$ = 100 psi

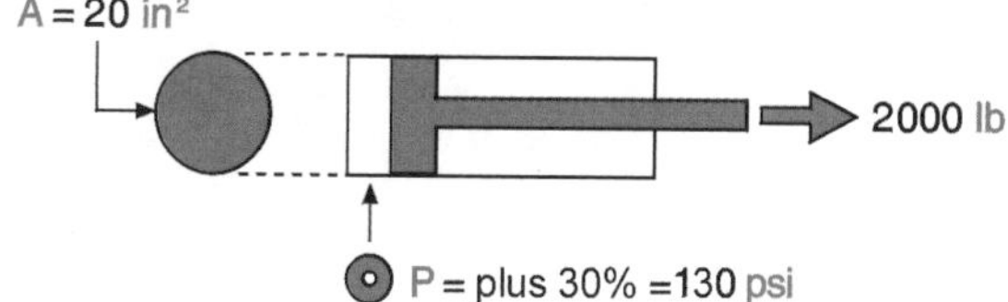

Example Calculation 4

$P_1 V_1 = P_2 V_2$

$V_2 = \frac{P_1 V_1}{P_2}$

P_1 =5.3 psig + 14.7 psi = 20 psi absolute
P_2 =85.3 psig + 14.7 psi = 100 psi absolute
V_1 =100 cu ft
V_2=?

$V_2 = \frac{20 \times 100}{100} = 20$ cu ft

Example Calculation 5

$P_1 V_1 = P_2 V_2$

P_1 = 0 bar gauge + 1 bar
= 1bar absolute

$P_2 = \frac{P_1 V_2}{V_2}$

P_2 = 1 x 1000 = 10 bar absolute

= 10 bar absolute - 1 bar
= 9 bar gauge

In Boyle's Law the **temperature** remains constant.

$P_1 V_1 = P_2 V_2 = C$

4. What is the final volume (V_2) of compressed air available at a pressure (P_2) of 85.3 psig?

The initial pressure (P_1) is 5.3 psig and initial volume (V_1) of air is 100 cubic feet. Note that the pressures used in Boyle's Law are in absolute units.

Therefore, 14.7 psi of atmospheric pressure must be added to the gauge pressure to give absolute pressure.

It is shown from the calculation that as pressure increases, volume decreases.

5. What is the final **gauge pressure (P_2)** in a compressed air system when the initial **pressure (P_1)** is 0 bar gauge?

Initial volume (V_1) is 1000 liters and the final **Volume (V_2)** is 100 liters.

We must convert 0 bar gauge to **absolute**. This is done by adding 1 bar **atmospheric**.

To give the answer in bar gauge, 1 bar atmospheric must be subtracted from the final absolute pressure in the calculation.

Note: 1.013 BAR is actual atmospheric pressure, but for calculation purposes 1 **bar** is used.

Components

Actuators

For compressed air to do useful work, its energy must be converted into a different, more usable form. This is normally mechanical force and motion.

This motion can be linear, limited rotary or rotary.

The components that produce this motion are called **actuators**.

Linear actuation is achieved by air **cylinders** or **rams**.

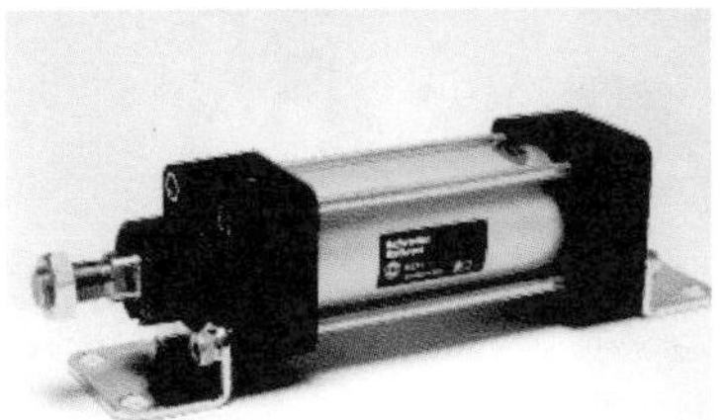

These house a piston attached to a piston rod.

The cylinder converts the energy of the compressed air into linear motion which will extend or retract the piston rod.

Cylinders or linear actuators come in all shapes and sizes.

They can be **single acting** which are normally returned to their original position by a spring or external force, such as gravity, or **double acting** in which both the extension of the piston and its return are powered by compressed air energy.

Cylinders convert pneumatic energy into **linear motion** which produces **force** and **velocity** (speed).

Cylinders, rotary actuators and motors are all examples of **pneumatic actuators**.

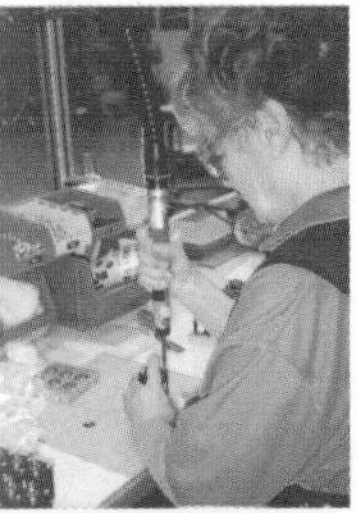

Limited rotary motion can be achieved by incorporating a rack and pinion into a linear actuator or as seen opposite by a **vane mechanism** within the body of the cylinder.

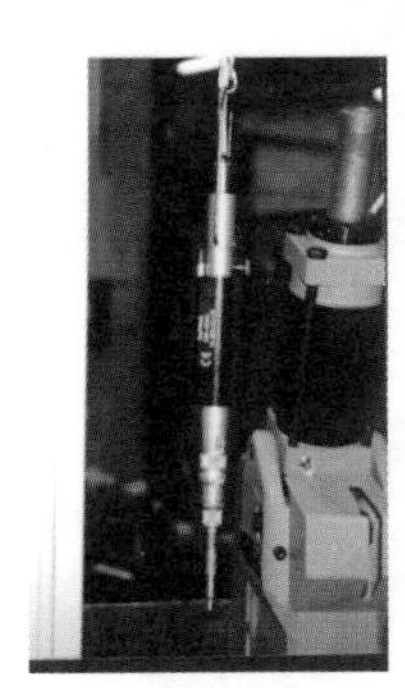

Rotary motion can also be produced by **air motors**. They can be large and robust to produce a high **torque** (rotary force).

Some smaller motors are capable of up to 20,000 revolutions per minute (rpm) such as used by dentists.

Air motors are used widely in industry where rotary motion energy is required.

Valves

To function efficiently and safely, the movement of actuators needs to be precisely controlled.

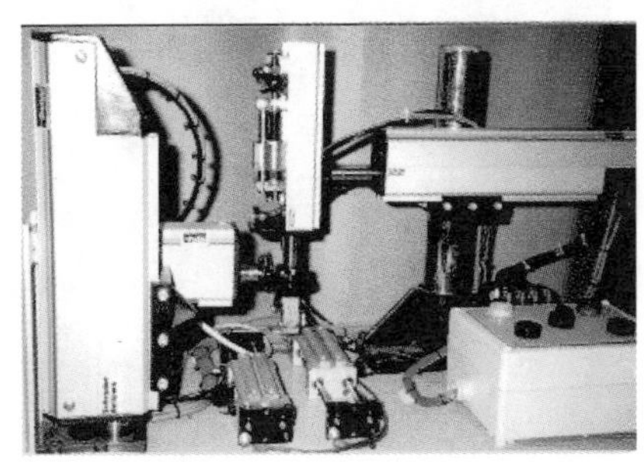

They must:
- move at the correct time
- move in the right direction
- move at the correct velocity
- produce the required force or torque

This control is provided by various valves in pneumatic systems.

These can be subdivided into thee basic types:

- direction
- flow
- pressure

Compressors

For air to do work in a typical industrial environment it should be compressed to around 100-120 psi (6.9 - 8.3 bar).

A typical truck compressed air system would be around 62.5 psi (4.5 bar) and a garage compressed air system would be up to 145 psi (10 bar).

An example of a simple compressor would be a bicycle or car tire pump. However, the pressure and flow are not sufficient for industrial use.

Industrial pneumatic systems generally supply pressurized air generated by large mechanical compressor.

Such compressors are driven by a prime mover. This can be an electric motor or the engine of a vehicle.

Compressors come in various types and sizes.

Portable compressors can be used where the volume of air required is low such as in small workshops and garages.

Oil free compressors, together with the correct filtration to remove other contaminants are used where cleanliness is of paramount importance.

These are generally used in the food and pharmaceutical industries. Mobile compressors which can be moved from site to site supply compressed air to operate equipment used in the construction industry.

Aftercoolers

Amongst other things, air contains moisture. This moisture is in the form or water vapour (vapor).

It will remain in this form as long as the temperature does not fall. For example, the film that covers a car windshield on a cold morning is moisture or water vapour (vapor) that has condensed from the atmosphere.

Unfortunately this is exactly what happens as warm compressed air cools in pipelines, exhaust devices and other equipment. As a consequence, the water vapour (vapor) condenses to form water droplets in the system.

In freezing conditions these droplets will solidify. If water has not been removed from, say an outside air receiver or piping system, the ice formed inside could place undue stresses on the unit.

Water droplets are detrimental to pneumatic equipment.

They corrode metal pipes and fittings and cause valves and cylinder seals to deteriorate.

They can wash away lubrication in valves, cylinders and other pneumatic components and equipment.

Aftercoolers are placed after the compressor to deliberately cool the air and remove some of the water from the air before it enters the system.

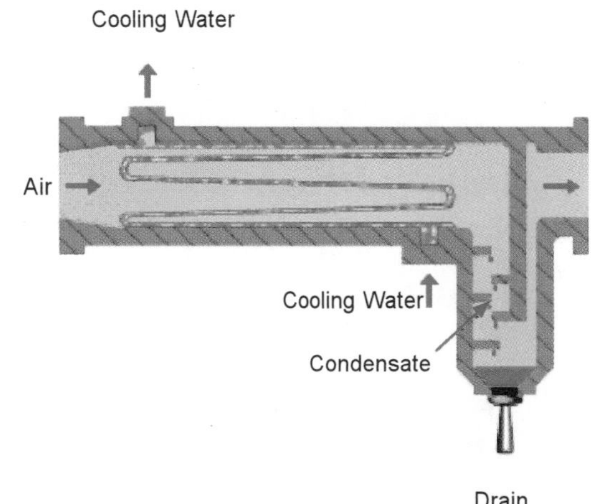

Aftercoolers come in various types and sizes depending upon the air flow capacity.

There are two basic types of aftercooler:

- air cooled
- water cooled

Air Receivers

Air receivers are used in most industrial pneumatic systems for storing compressed air until it is required.

A receiver tank assures a steady air supply which can reduce pressure pulsations and frequent loading/unloading of the compressor.

Air receivers are the equivalent of a battery in an electrical system or an accumulator in a hydraulic system.

If sized and positioned correctly it can assist in water removal by cooling the air.

Air receivers also help to remove other contaminants such as dirt particles and oil.

Pressure Vessel codes and regulations are very strict as to the strength and testing of these devices.

Because of this, they need to be drained, inspected and tested at regular intervals to ensure that they are not corroded or damaged in any way.

Air receivers must have a working pressure gauge to show the pressure within the pressure vessel.

Air receivers must also have a means of discharging the full rated flow of the compressor(s) if supplied at too high a pressure.

This is normally in the form of a **safety relief valve**.

Some compressed air systems require very dry air; for example, in the food industry.

Therefore, all moisture must be removed. This is done by a **dryer** placed in the system.

There are three main types of dryers:

- Absorbtion or Deliquescent
- Adsorbtion or Desiccant
- Refrigerant

Air dryers are not cheap.

However, moisture can damage components in compressed air systems resulting in loss of production due to unscheduled maintenance and down time.

Moisture in paint spraying systems could be catastrophic especially in the automobile industry.

Filters

Filters are essential items in compressed air system. Small particles of contaminants can cause serious malfunction of pneumatic components and must, therefore, be removed.

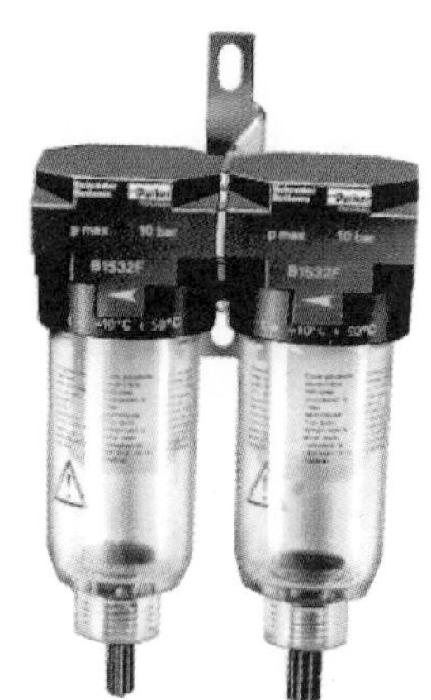

Contaminants are broadly classified as **hard**, **soft** and **fluid**.

These contaminants include water, smoke, corrosive fumes, bacteria, viruses, gases, oil, solids and dirt.

Excluding these from compressed air systems can help to ensure that the system works efficiently, economically, safely and trouble free for a long time.

Regulators

All compressed air systems must work **efficiently** and **safely**.

Of prime importance here is that the pressure in the system be properly **regulated**.

It is this **pressure** that determines force or torque on a cylinder or motor.

If it is too high, it may exceed safe limits.

It may also be inefficient. If the pressure is set above that required to supply adequate force to the actuators in the system, the energy is not being used efficiently.

The working pressure for each machine in a system should be set by a **pressure regulator**.

This maintains the system pressure at a constant safe and efficient level.

Lubricators / Combined Units

During manufacture many valves and cylinders are pre-lubricated. However, this may eventually be removed over time.

Most moving parts have to be lubricated to reduce friction and increase their performance and life.

Lubricators, when placed in the correct position, will maximize the working life of equipment.

Consideration should be taken to ensure that the correct lubricants are used in the right amount.

Filters, regulators & lubricators can be combined to ensure optimum compressed air preparation for a specific pneumatic system.

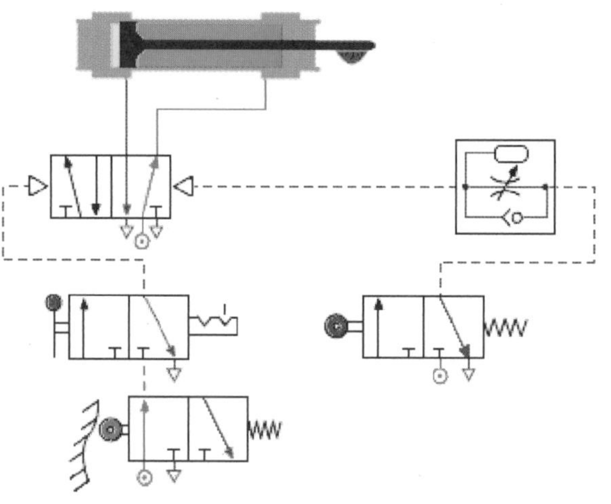

Symbols and Standards

All pneumatic systems can be represented by circuit diagrams, in much the same way that an electrical engineer maps an electrical system.

These can be either pictorial or schematic drawings.

Generally a symbol represents a single component, with several components joined by lines which represent pipe work.

In schematic drawings the symbols used should be universal, so that engineers in different countries can understand any circuit drawing.

International
Standards
Organisation

The International Standards Organisation (ISO) has established such a set of symbols and these should be used whenever possible. Symbols should be to the current Standard ISO 1219.

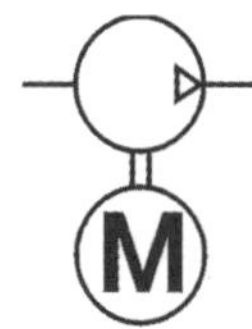

Compressors

Circles enclosing open triangles denote compressors. The triangle indicates the direction of the compressed air or gas flow.

The type of prime mover is indicated by adding its symbol to the compressor symbol. For example, the symbol shown opposite is that of an electric motor.

Actuators

A range of shapes can denote an actuator. If the actuator is a cylinder, sometimes called a **ram**, a rectangle is drawn. A piston is then drawn inside the rectangle, connected to a piston rod. If the cylinder is powered in one direction only, i.e., is **single acting**, the entry / exit port for the compressed air is denoted by a small line.

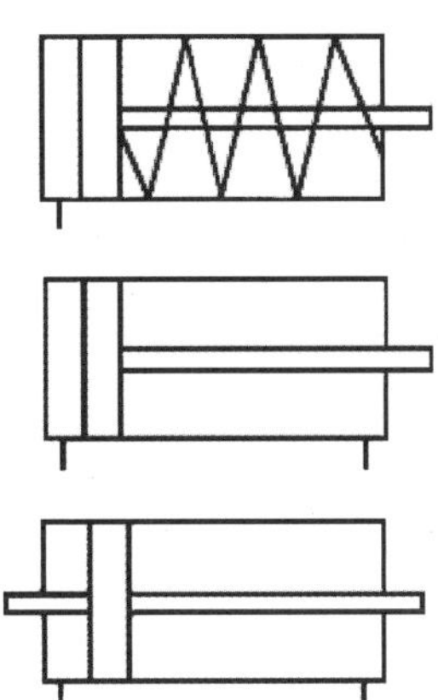

There are a number of variations on this basic actuator symbol. Show here are:

- A single acting cylinder with spring return
- A double acting cylinder
- A double rod cylinder (through rodded)

The **double acting** cylinder is probably the most common type of actuator used in pneumatic systems.

Rotary Actuators

If the actuator is an **air motor**, a circle is drawn. A triangle is then drawn inside the circle.

The triangle, in the motor symbol, is oriented in the opposite direction to that found in a compressor symbol, as compressed air or gas drives the motor.

Shown here are:

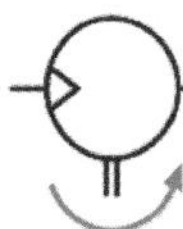

- A single direction of rotation motor
- A bidirectional rotation motor, which can rotate in either direction

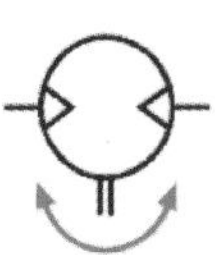

Valves

Valves are symbolized in different ways depending upon their role in the circuit.

Valves may control:

- direction
- flow rate (velocity)

Flow Control Valves

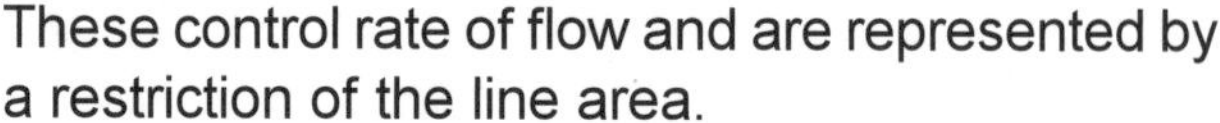

These control rate of flow and are represented by a restriction of the line area.

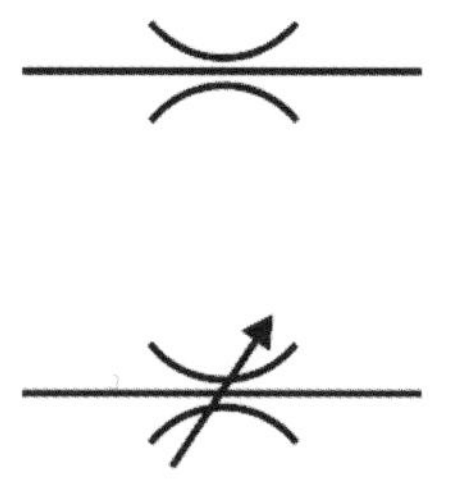

If the valve has a fixed setting, the line is bounded by two semicircles.

If the valve setting is adjustable, this is shown with an arrow diagonally drawn through the main line and semicircles.

Directional Control Valves

One type of directional control is the check valve or non return valve. This allows compressed air to flow in one direction only.

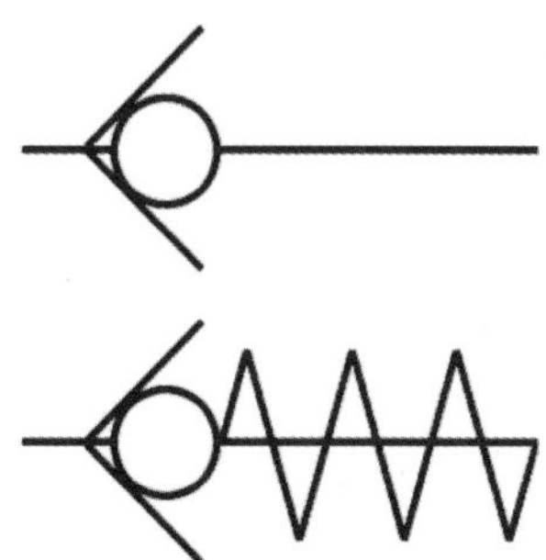

These may be:

- free
- spring loaded

Other directional control valves 'open' or 'close' various flow paths for the compressed air.

The terms 'open' and 'closed' may be replaced with 'passing' and 'non-passing' to reduce the possibility of confusion with the electrical terms 'open' and 'closed' where the meanings are reversed.

i.e., 'open' in pneumatics means a flow path through the valve; in electrics, there is no current flowing.

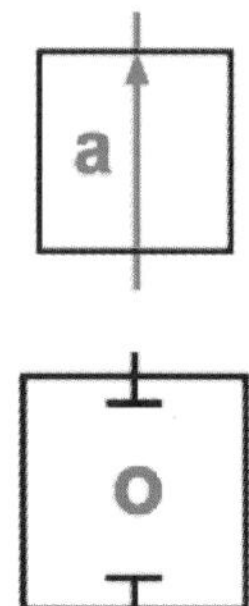

These valves are characterized by two features.

The first feature is the number of ports for air to enter and leave the valve.

Position "a", the **actuated** position, shows a single flow path as shown by the single arrow. It therefore has 2 ports, an inlet and an outlet port.

In position "o", the neutral or at rest position, the two ports are closed. Therefore, air flow is stopped.

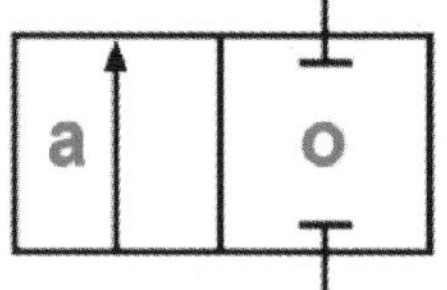

The second feature is the number of operating positions for the valve. This is shown by a corresponding number of squares.

Thus a valve with two positions is represented by two squares side by side.

Each position is identified by letters such as "a" and "o."

The designation for the valve shown is a 2/2 directional control valve. The first number refers to the number of ports while the second refers to the number of positions.

This vale has two main flow paths as shown by the two arrows.

Each path has two ports. Thus, the valve has four ports in all.

- one main port
- one exhaust port
- two working ports

There are two squares. Hence, there are two positions.

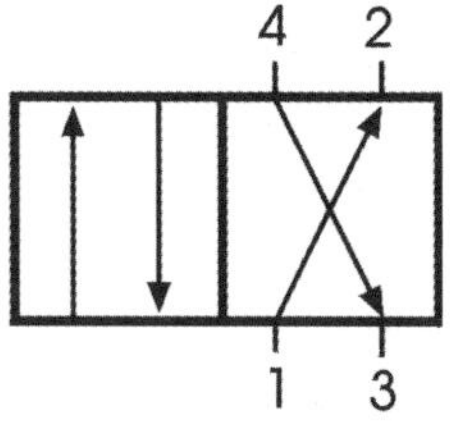

Therefore, it is a 4/2 directional control valve.

By convention the ports are marked:

1 - System / Pressure Port
3 - Exhaust Port
2, 4 - Load / Working Ports

Valve Actuators

Valves can be actuated in a number of ways. These controls are termed valve actuators.

The type of actuator is shown by a symbol attached to the sides of the squares.

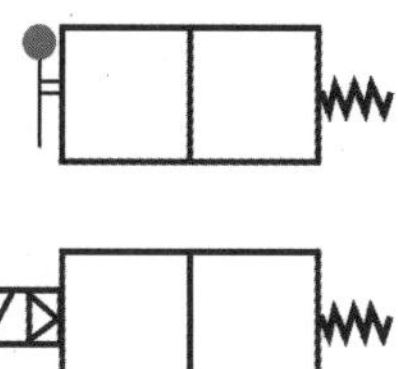

Here a manual actuator is shown and below it an electrical solenoid / air pilot actuator. Both valves return to the neutral position by a spring.

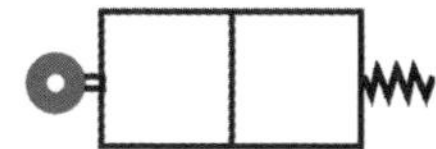

Shown opposite is a cam roller operated valve, with spring return to the neutral or at rest position.

Pipe Work

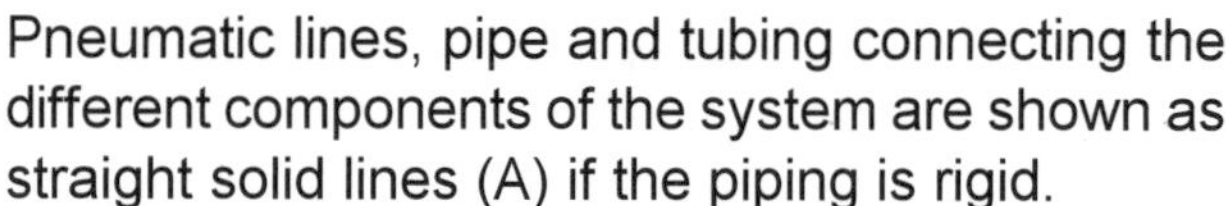

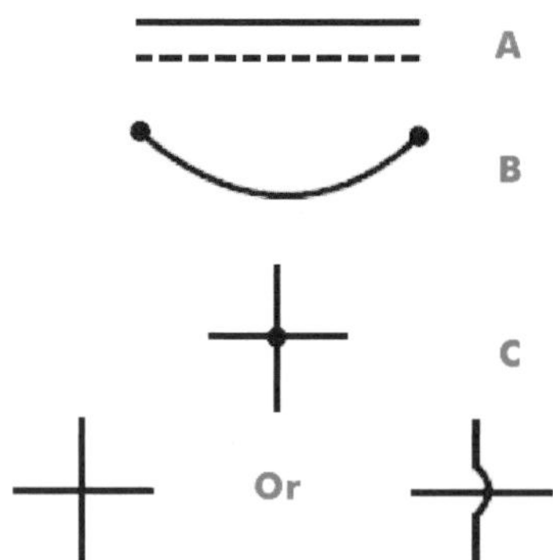

Pneumatic lines, pipe and tubing connecting the different components of the system are shown as straight solid lines (A) if the piping is rigid.

Pilot lines are always "dashed" lines (A). These are generally signal lines only.

If the pipe work is flexible, curved lines (B) are used. Line junctions (C) are shown by a small black circle at the point of intersection of the lines.

Lines crossing but not connected are shown with the black semicircle over the first line.

Storage

The air receiver is symbolized by the elliptical shape shown opposite.

Air Preparation

Units that prepare or condition the air are diamond shaped.

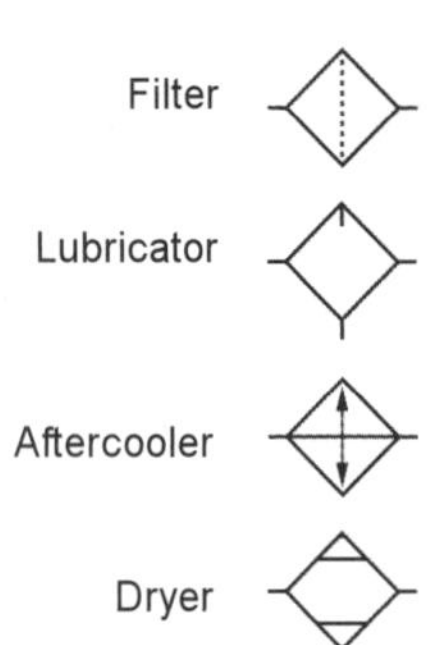

Shown here are:

- filter
- lubricator
- aftercooler
- dryer

Pressure Regulator

These are drawn as a single square with an arrow. This arrow shows the direction of flow through the valve.

The symbol here shows a double arrow allowing reverse flow of air to the triangle exhaust symbol. This is a vent type pressure regulator.

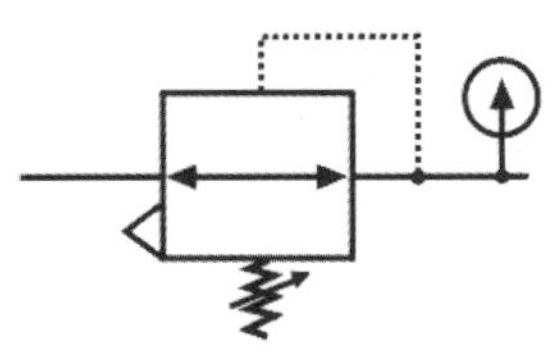

The non-vent type of pressure regulator has a single arrow and no exhaust triangle.

The dashed line indicates a **pilot** line, which senses the downstream of secondary pressure.

A pilot line shows in this way normally represents an internal connection within the component; there is not physical line connected to the downstream line.

Adjustment of the pressure setting on the **regulator** is shown by a spring with a diagonal arrow through it.

Filters, **regulators** and **lubricators** are usually combined to produce **FRLs**.

The simplified version of the symbol is shown here.

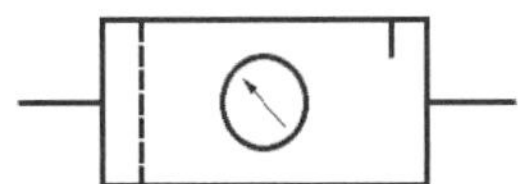

Meters and Gauges

Instruments to monitor the state of the air in the system are represented by circular symbols.

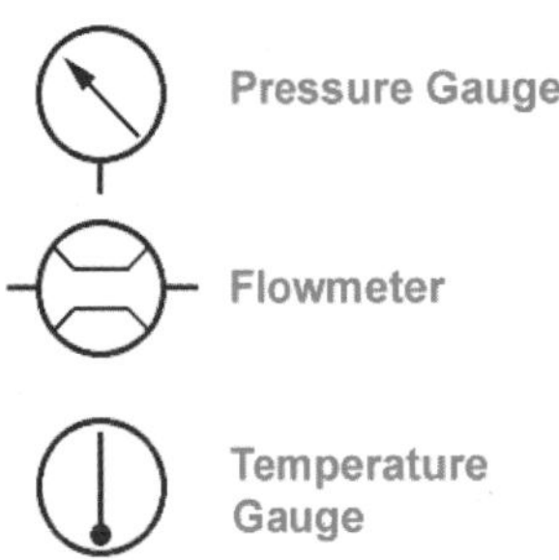

A pressure gauge is a circle, with an arrow inside it, which is mounted at right angles to the main line.

A flowmeter is a circle, containing two semicircles, which is mounted in the pneumatic line.

A temperature gauge is a circle with a vertical line inside it. At the base of the vertical line is a “bulb”.

Units

This table gives some of the units used to describe pneumatic systems.

The SI (System International) or ISO units, which should be used to describe flow, pressure, work and power, are given next to the corresponding US / Imperial units.

	SI Units	US Units
Distance per unit time	Meter per second m/s	Feet per second ft/s or f.p.s
Volume flow rate	Litres/second	Standard cubic feet/minute cu.ft/min or S.C.F.M
Pressure	Bar Pascal bar pa	pounds/sq. inch psi
Work done	Newton metres Nm	Foot pound force ft lbf
Power	Watt Kilowatt W KW	Horsepower hp
Force	Newton N	Pounds lb

Safety Procedures

There is no greater risk with compressed air or gas, than with any other industrial power source such as hydraulic or electric systems, as long as it is treated with respect.

Compressed air has an extremely high safety record compared with electrical systems. Health and safety legislation must be followed at all times.

Safety of compressed air is covered in Module 2.

Summary

- Pneumatics is the use of compressed air as a power source.
- Such systems are used extensively in industry.

Significant Properties of Gases

- Gases are **compressible**
- Gases are **elastic**

Gas Laws

- Boyle's Law states that the product of Pressure (P) and Volume (V) of a gas is a constant (C), provided the temperature does not vary.
- $P_1 \times V_1 = P_2 \times V_2 = C$
- Charles' / Gay Lussac's Law states that at a constant pressure, the Volume (V) of a gas increases in proportion to the Temperature (T).

  $$V_1 = V_2 \times \frac{T_1}{T_2} \text{ or } V_2 = V_1 \times \frac{T_2}{T_1}$$

- An alternative form of this law states that at a constant volume, the Pressure (P) of a gas increases with the Temperature (T).

  $$P_1 = P_2 \times \frac{T_1}{T_2} \text{ or } P_2 = P_1 \times \frac{T_2}{T_1}$$

- Pascal's Law states that force within a system is transmitted, undiminished, in all directions throughout the system.

  F = P x A

Components

- An **actuator** converts pneumatic force into mechanical force and action.

- **Valves** control the pressure of the air, the direction of flow of air and the rate of flow of air in a pneumatic system.

- **Compressors** pressurize the air in a pneumatic system.

- **Aftercoolers** remove some moisture from compressed air.

- **Air receivers** store compressed air.

- **Dryers** are incorporated into systems that require totally dry air.

- **Filters** protect the system from contaminants.

- **Pressure regulators** set the maximum working pressure in the system.

- **Lubricators** reduce friction in the system by adding oil to the air supply.

Symbols and Standards

- All pneumatic systems are represented by circuit diagrams.
- Components are represented by symbols established by the International Standards Organisation (ISO).

Safety

- There is a set of standard safety procedures which must be adopted to minimize the risks to personnel health and safety posed by pneumatic systems.
- Particular attention should be paid to minimizing noise pollution which can pose a threat to health and safety.

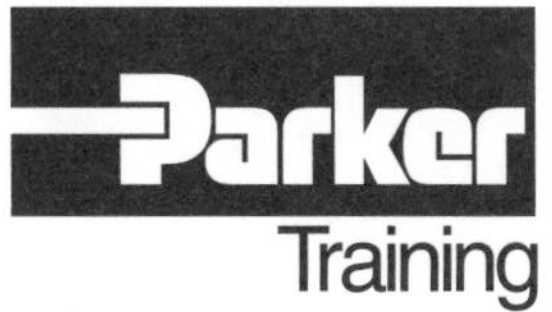

Module 2

Compressed Air Production

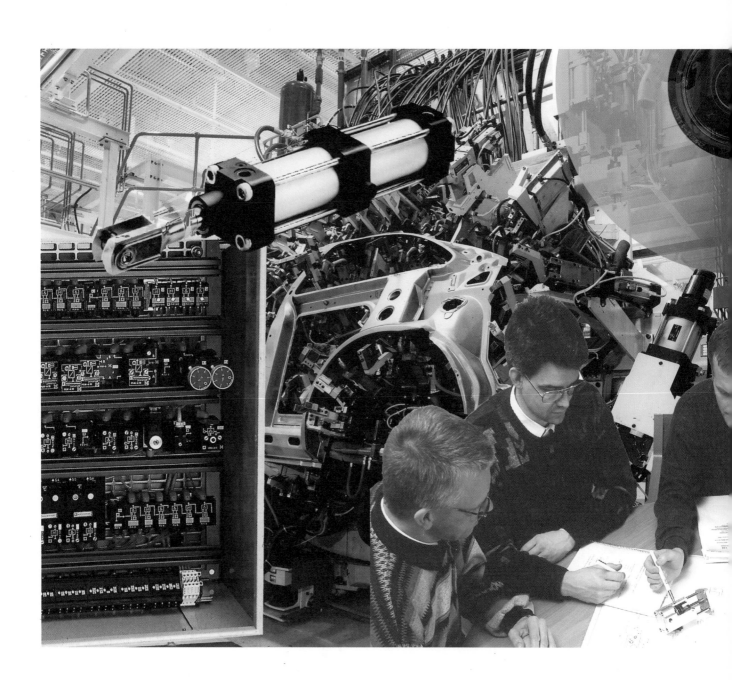

Contents

Compressed Air Production, Preparation, Distribution And Safe Use

Objectives

In this section the following will be examined:

- different types of compressors, including reciprocating, diaphragm, vane and screw
- selection of compressors
- the construction and function of air receivers

COMPRESSORS
Dynamic
Displacement
Radial
Axial
Rotary
Reciprocating
Vane
Screw
Lobe
Trunk
Crosshead
Free Piston
Labyrinth
Diaphragm

Compressors

Compressors are generally categorized by type.

The two main types are:

- displacement
- dynamic

Displacement compressors confine atmospheric air in a chamber.

The volume of the chamber is gradually reduced.

This compresses and pressurizes the air.

Dynamic compressors draw atmospheric air in and compress it by accelerating the air mass.

The pressure is increased by adding kinetic energy to accelerate the mass of air, then converting the velocity energy into pressure energy.

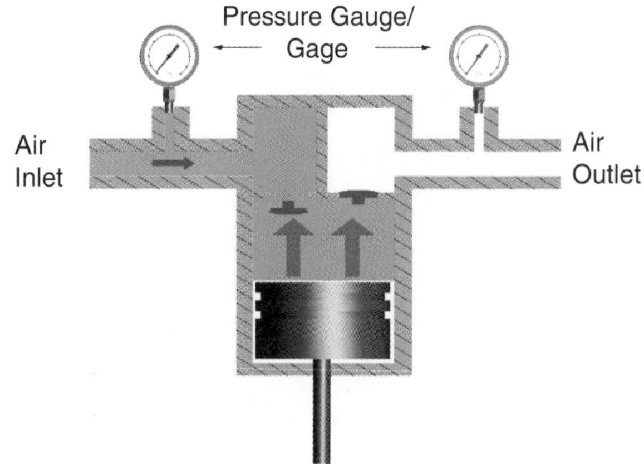

Displacement Compressor

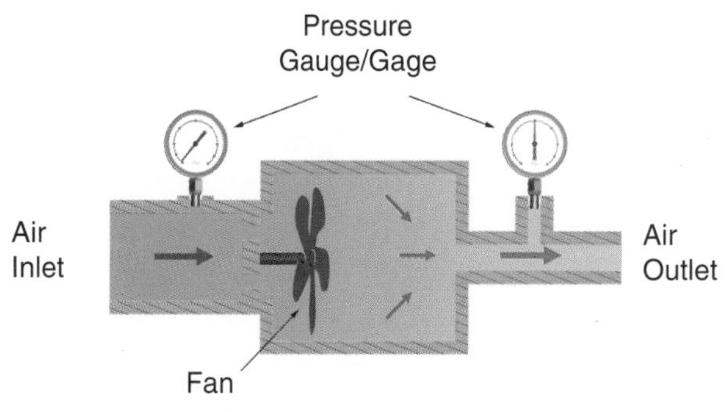

Dynamic Compressor

Although the two categories of compressors differ in design they both have the same function:

To take a volume of air at atmospheric pressure and compress it to a predetermined higher level of pressure.

Reciprocating Compressor

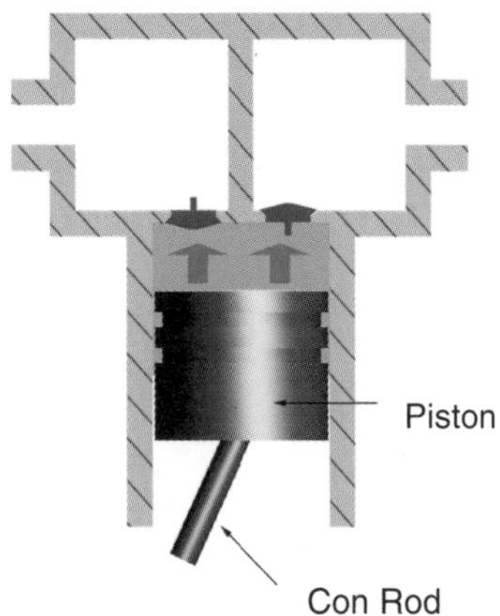

This type is widely used in industry and can be single stage or multi-stage.

The single stage compressor, commonly found in vehicles and small workshops, compresses the air in a single piston stroke.

The compressed air is then discharged into the system.

A typical pressure supplied by this type of compressor is 10 bar or 145 psi.

In this type of compressor a cylinder bore encloses a moving piston.

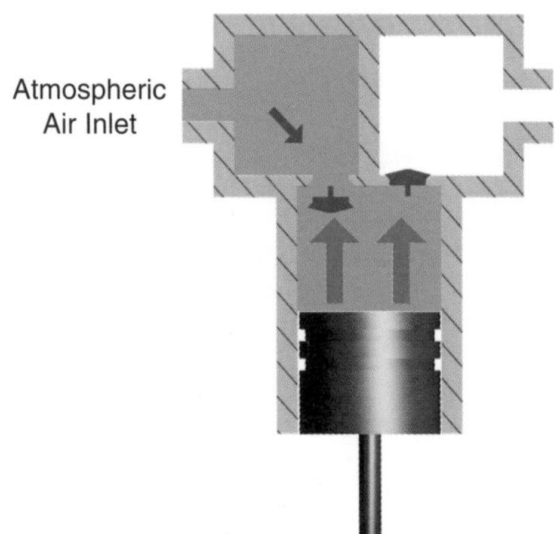

As the crankshaft of the compressor rotates, the piston moves within the cylinder chamber, similar to the pistons in a car engine.

As the piston is pulled down, the volume increases, creating a lower atmospheric pressure in the piston chamber.

This difference in pressure causes air to enter via the inlet valve.

As the piston is forced upwards the volume of air reduces. The air pressure therefore increases.

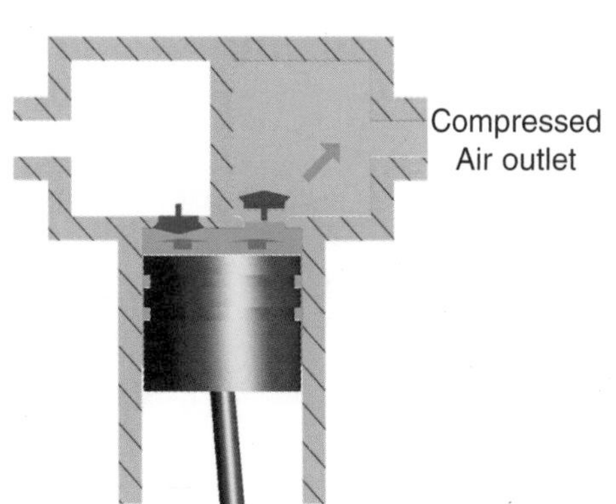

Eventually the pressure forces the outlet valve to open.

The compressed air is then discharged.

Whenever air is compressed heat is generated.

This increases the energy required to compress the air.

To avoid an excessive rise in temperature, **multi-stage** compressors with **intercoolers** have been developed. These compressors can generate higher pressures than single stage compressors.

The most common type is the **two-stage** compressor. This consists of 2 pistons, one large, one small, each in its own cylinder bore and connected to the same crankshaft.

An **intercooler** is placed between the two cylinder bores.

Air is drawn into the large cylinder bore which is then compressed by the piston to a predetermined pressure.

The outlet valve then opens, discharging the hot air into the intercooler.

The air is then cooled, either by cold water flowing through the pipes in the intercooler or by air blown across it by a fan.

The cooled, compressed air enters the smaller second stage cylinder bore via the inlet valve.

As the piston moves in the bore, the air is further compressed, increasing the pressure. The outlet valve then opens allowing the air to pass into the system.

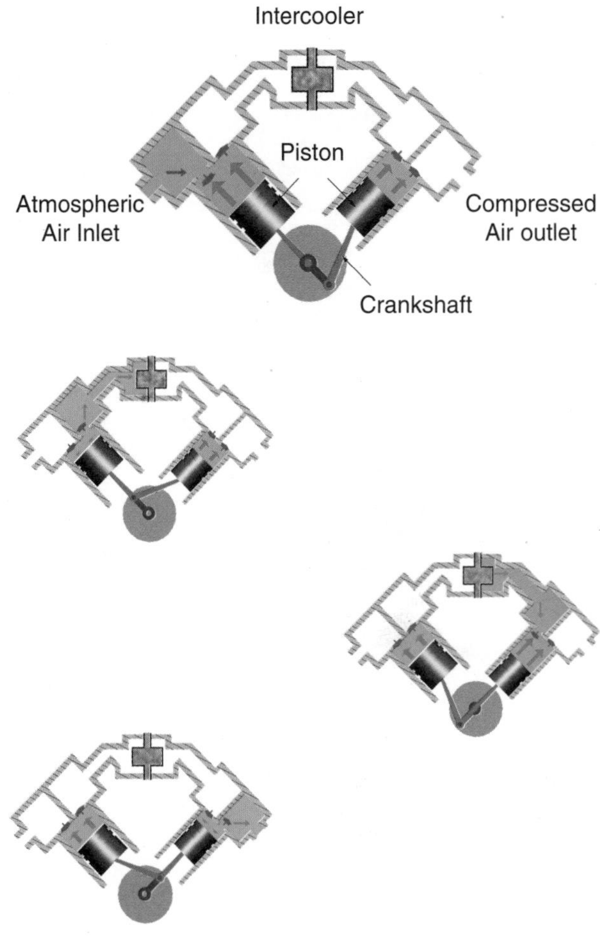

Diaphragm Compressor

The diaphragm compressor works on the same principle as the piston compressor, but the piston is separated from the compression chamber by a diaphragm.

This diaphragm prevents the air from coming into contact with the reciprocating parts, keeping the air totally free of oil.

This type of compressor is ideal for the food, pharmaceutical and similar industries where compressed air must be free from oil.

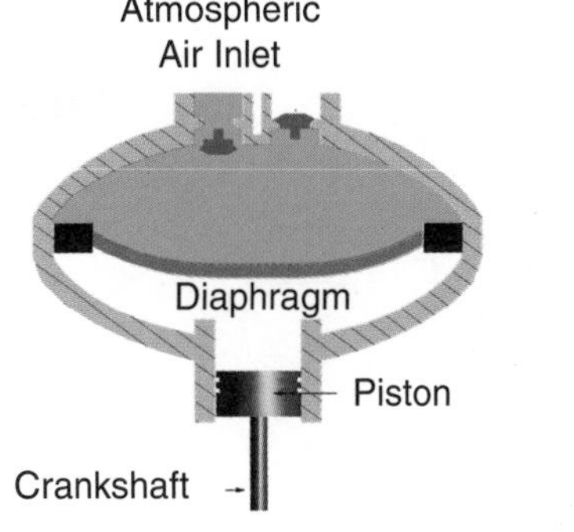

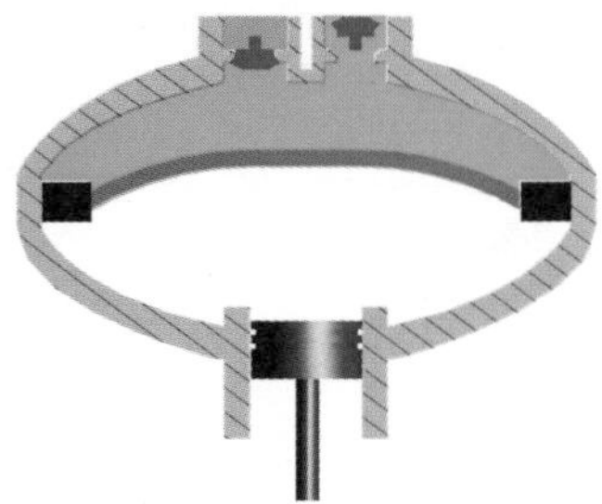

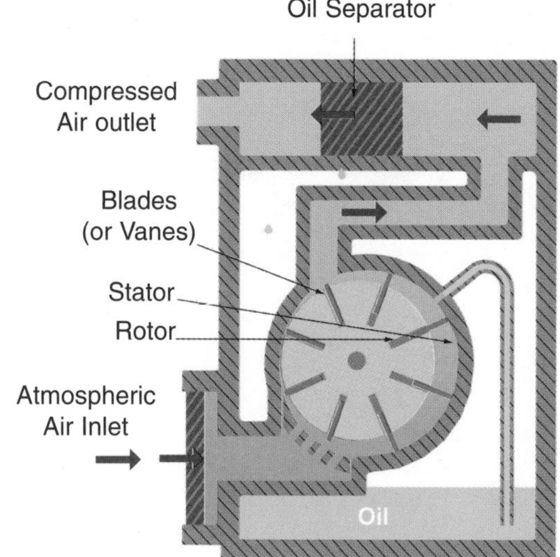

Rotary Compressor

The **rotary compressor**, also called a **vane** compressor, is highly efficient but has a pressure limitation of approximately 10 bar/145 psi.

The **rotor** is mounted off center in the compression chamber or **stator**. This allows the volume of air to decrease in the chamber.

The rotor is attached by a shaft to a driving device, usually an electric motor, and has a number of slots, each containing a blade or vane.

As the rotor turns, the vanes are thrown out against the stator wall by centrifugal force.

A seal is formed by oil between the rotor and stator which is injected into the air early in the compression cycle. This oil is later removed from the air by an oil separator.

The air inlet is placed where the volume of the compression chamber is greatest, the outlet where the volume is smallest.

Consequently, as the vanes turn, the space between them is reduced.

This reduction in volume compresses the air as it travels from the inlet to the outlet.

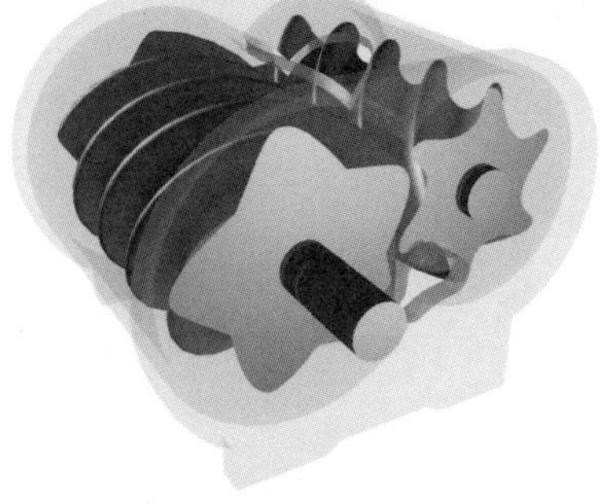

Rotary Screw Compressor

The rotary screw compressor has two intermeshing screws with helical lobes.

Pressures up to 10 bar/145 psi are achieved as well as high flow rates by these very quiet compressors.

As the screws revolve, the space between the lobes decreases. This compresses the air at the outlet port.

Precise positioning of the screws is essential and oil provides a seal between the rotating screws as well as lubricating the parts and cooling the air.

The oil is then separated from the air before it enters the system.

Lobed Rotor

In this type of compressor the rotors do not touch and a certain amount of 'slip' exists. This 'slip' increases as the output pressure increases.

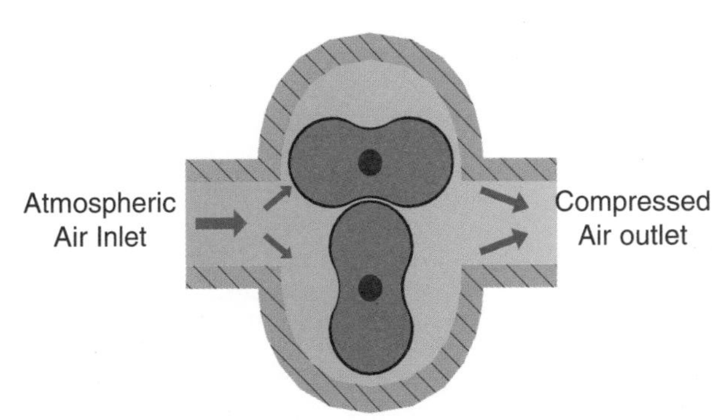

It is therefore operated at maximum speed for the highest efficiency.

17.3 bar (250 psi) is obtainable with this type of constant displacement compressor.

It is vital for the effective and efficient running of a compressed air plant that the appropriate compressor is selected to meet the system needs.

Large compressor installations can be expensive and complex and assistance should be sought from a specialist.

However, the following points should always be considered:

System Demand

This should include both the estimated initial loading and near term loading.

Standby Capacity for Emergencies

This can be a second compressor connected to the system which starts automatically if a malfunction occurs.

Or it can be a separate connection built into the main system to allow a mobile or auxiliary compressor to be connected.

Future Air Requirement

Any compressor installation must take into account any anticipated future requirements.

Air Receivers

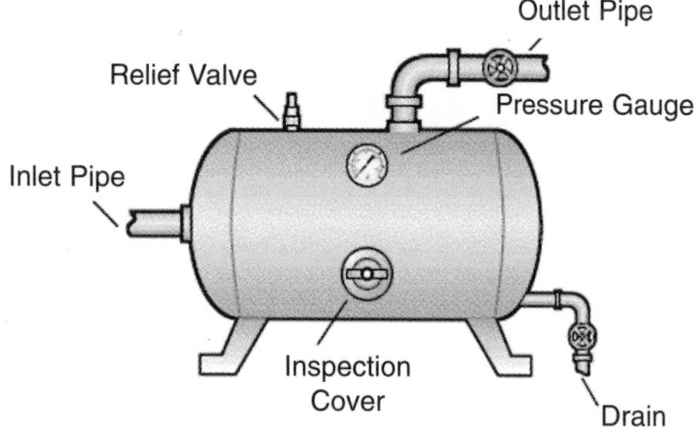

Air receivers, as their name suggests, accept and hold the air delivered by the compressor.

They are pressure vessels and are subject to regular inspections by qualified personnel, and they must be constructed and conform to current National / International and local legislation standards.

They play a vital role in a compressed air system, and must have:

- a pressure relief valve
- pressure gauge
- inspection cover
- drain valve

Their functions include:

Damp the pulsating air delivery from the compressor.

Holding sufficient compressed air to provide a steady air supply to the system without excessive pressure fluctuations when demand varies.

Storing compressed air which satisfies intermittent heavy demands in excess of compressor capacity.

Providing additional cooling and drainage facilities for moisture and contamination removal.

Allowing the compressor to *work efficiently* by minimizing the load/unload time.

Summary

Compressors

- Compressors are of two types. Displacement compressors pressurize the air by reducing its volume. Dynamic compressors pressurize the air by accelerating the air mass.

- Reciprocating compressors are displacement compressors that pressurizes the air by the action of a piston moving in a cylinder bore.

- The diaphragm compressor is a displacement compressor that pressurizes air by the action of a diaphragm and is generally oil free.

- The rotary compressor pressurizes air by the action of a rotor and vanes revolving within a stator.

- The rotary screw compressor pressurizes air by the action of two helical screws.

- A lobed rotor compressor is a high speed compressor which gives a constant displacement of air.

- Compressor selection must be based upon system demand, emergency standby capacity, and any anticipated future demand.

Receivers

- Air receivers damp pulsations and store sufficient air to meet occasional heavy demands.

- They also provide additional cooling and drainage facilities. They must incorporate pressure relief valves (safety valves) to ensure that maximum system pressure is not exceeded.

Air Preparation

Objectives

In this section the following will be examined:

- The cooling, drying and filtration of air used in pneumatic systems.

- The regulation of air pressure.

- The lubrication of the moving parts in a pneumatic system.

Atmospheric air contains a mixture of contaminants which can affect the efficiency and working life span of pneumatic systems. These include:

- water vapour (vapor)
- dust
- fumes
- bacteria

Other contaminants can be added during compression of the air. These include:

- compressor lubricant

- fragments arising from the wear and tear of the compressor and distribution system

Here is a chart highlighting the various contaminants.

Contaminant	Source	Entry To System
Water Vapour	Atmosphere	Via Compressor
Dust, Smoke, Fumes	Atmosphere	Via Compressor
Bacteria, Viruses	Atmosphere	Via Compressor
Gases	Compressor	Generated In Compressor
Oil	Compressor	From Compressor
Solids	Compressor Piping	From Compressor Airlines

To prevent deterioration of the system and its components by abrasive particles, moisture and oil, air preparation equipment is incorporated into the system.

These systems must remove particles measured on a microscopic scale.

Often these particles measure around 40 microns. A filter can remove particulate contaminants as small as 5 microns.

For reference, the diameter of human hair is around 70 microns.

A grain of salt is around 100 micron in size. A micron is also known as a micrometer.

1 MICRON (um) = 0.001 mm = 0.00004 "

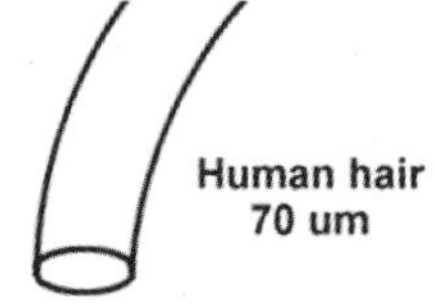

Moisture

All air contains some moisture in the form of water vapour (vapor). We record this as the humidity of the air or a vapour (vapor) pressure.

As long as this moisture remains in the vapour (vapor) state, it poses little problem to pneumatic systems.

However the amount of water which air can hold in the vapour (vapor) state is dependent upon the temperature of that air.

As shown opposite, the higher the temperature, the greater the moisture that can be held. Therefore if the air is cooled, some of that water condenses out of the air to form a liquid.

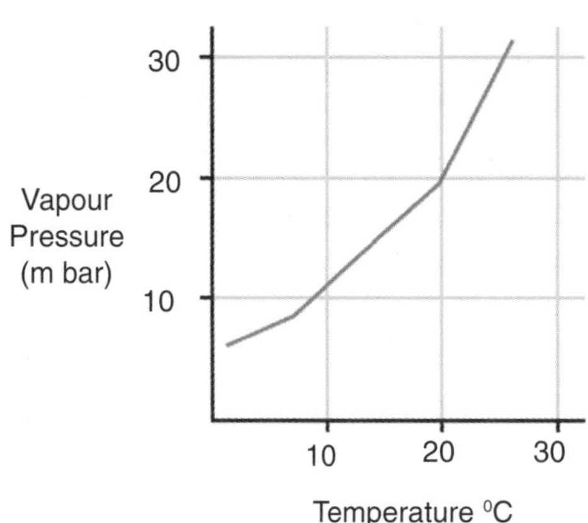

Such air cooling and condensation is a common feature of air compression systems and can cause damage. It can wash away lubrication and cause corrosion of the airline which will lead to leaks and expensive replacement.

It may cause damage to pneumatic components and control systems within machinery.

Incorrect operation of machine control systems can result, which could be dangerous.

Filters may be saturated with contaminants and become blocked, along with drainage points, which leads to reduced airline efficiency.

This in turn could lead to air starvation and system malfunction.

Overall, such water contamination will greatly increase maintenance costs.

If the system is outside, for example, in a vehicle, the water could freeze, damaging the system.

Here, antifreeze, normally methanol in a gaseous form, could be added. However care must be taken to ensure full compatibility with the equipment in the system. Moisture in the form of water may wash away lubricants and cause valves and equipment to malfunction.

This moisture must be removed from the air.

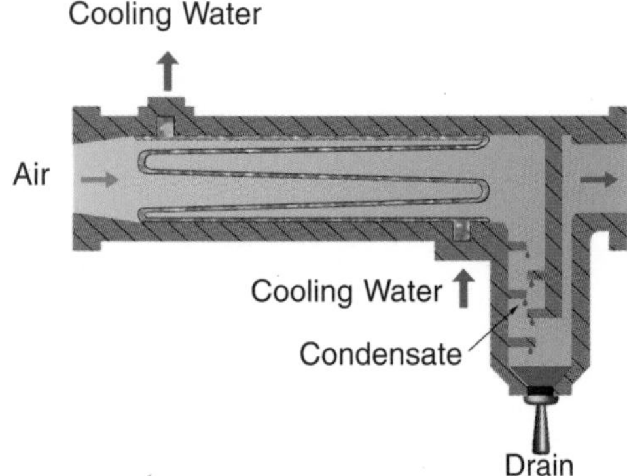

Condensate is best removed when the air pressure is at its highest and the air temperature at its lowest.

Therefore removal should take place immediately after the air leaves the compressor or as soon as practical.

The **aftercooler** can be an integral part of the compressor or can be a stand alone item. The heat exchanger uses either water or air as the cooling medium.

As the air passes over the cooling media, in this case water pipes, the drop in air temperature causes water to condense out of the air. This water can then be drained off manually or automatically.

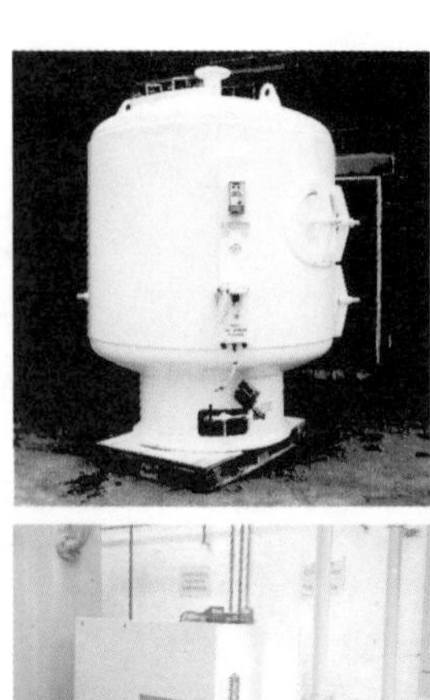

In systems requiring extremely dry air a **dryer** should be used.

Factors which are important in determining the correct air dryer include:

- air temperature
- dryer flow capacity
- air velocity

There are 3 main types of dryers - **Absorption**, **Adsorbtion** and **Refrigerant**.

Deliquescent or Absorption Dryer

This dryer passes the compressed air over a drying agent, which chemically combines with the water in the air and settles to the bottom of the drying vessel.

Chemicals used include:

- Dehydrated chalk
- Magnesium perchlorate
- Lithium chloride
- Calcium chloride

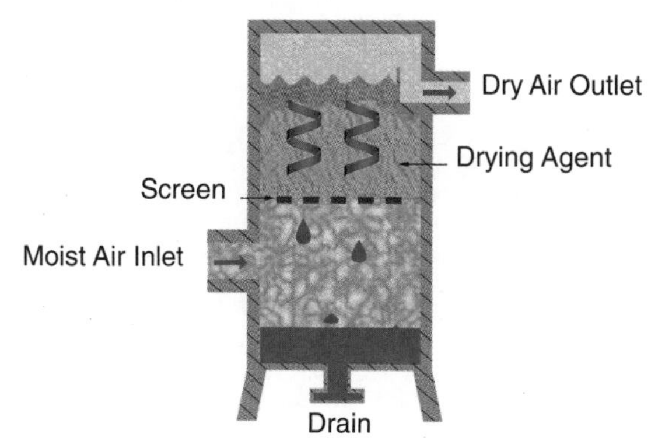

The chemical must be replaced at regular intervals to ensure maximum efficiency.

The liquid in the tank should be drained regularly as the fluid is highly corrosive and can give some problems.

The desiccant pellets can soften and bake at temperatures exceeding 32°C (90°F).

In this type of dryer a pressure drop may be caused by the moisture in the drying agent and in addition a fine corrosive mist may be carried downstream.

Desiccant or Adsorbtion Dryer

This uses a physical process with the drying agent being of granular form, most commonly silica gel or actuated alumina.

Wet compressed air passes over the granules, and the adsorption chemicals hold water vapour (vapor) in small pores.

When the granules become saturated they can be regenerated by heat.

This requires two drying plants in parallel.

This type of air drying is the most costly. There is a high initial cost and high operating costs.

Opposite, the drying plant on the left is being used, while the one on the right is being regenerated.

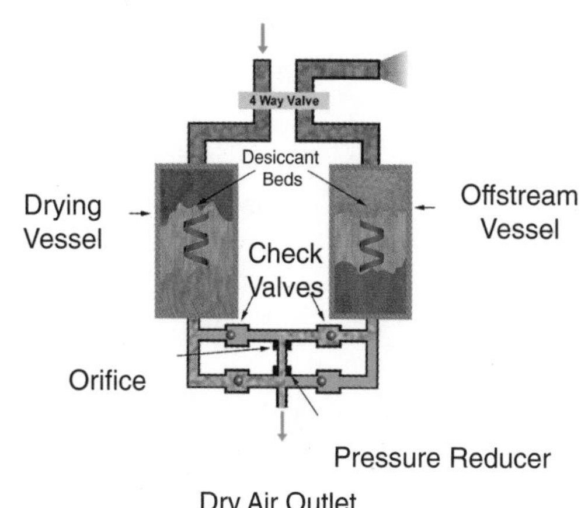

Refrigerated Dryer

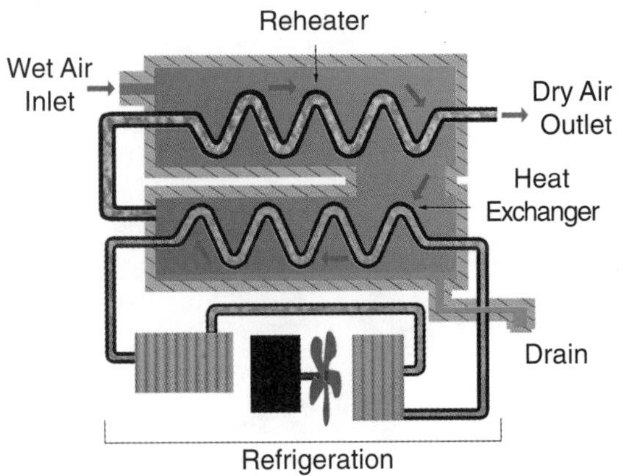

This works by lowering the temperature of the air to a point, called the **dew point**, where the water vapour (vapor) condenses from the compressed air.

Condensate is formed in the heat exchanger as the air comes into contact with the refrigeration unit.

The condensate is drained away manually or automatically.

This condensate must **never** be poured down a drain as it may be heavily contaminated with oil etc.

Contact with the refrigeration unit cools the air to dry it.

This can be as low as 32.4°F (0.6°C). It must not go lower as frost may form. A typical temperature would be 50°F (10°C). If the air is passed straight into the system, this low temperature could cause water to condense on the outside of the pipes in the system, if the ambient factory air temperature was higher. This could lead to external corrosion and must be prevented.

Therefore the air is directed through a re-heater to ensure that such external corrosion does not happen.

Filters

Intake Filters

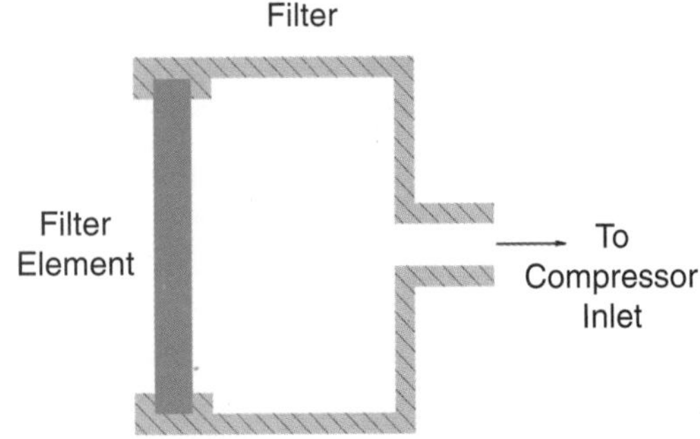

Care must be taken to minimize the entry of contaminants into the system. First, the air should preferably be drawn from outside, to prevent any factory generated contaminants.

Secondly, the air intake should not be situated where dust etc. can be generated by vehicles and passing traffic.

An air intake filter is connected to the air inlet port of the compressor to prevent solid contaminants entering the compression chamber of the compressor.

The efficiency of intake filters can vary but can be as high as 99% efficient.

Intake filters must be checked and maintained regularly. Air starvation of a compressor can result if a filter becomes blocked.

Such starvation reduces the efficiency of the system and can damage the compressor.

Airline Filters

Airline filters come in all sizes. They are placed at various points within a system. Important equipment such as dryers and the pneumatic control systems of machinery must be protected from contaminants.

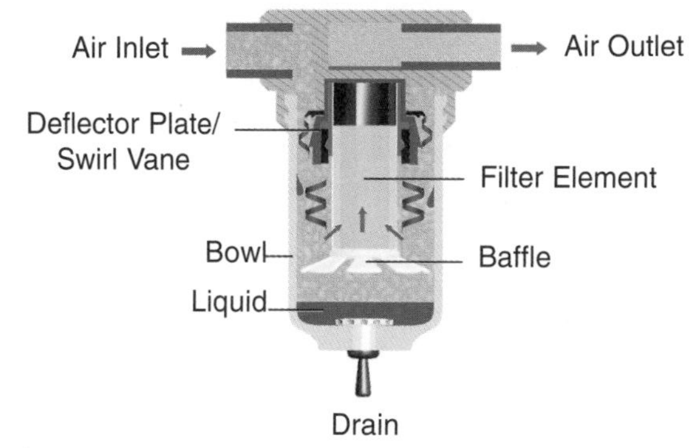

Auxiliary or secondary lines also require filters to protect machine tool pneumatic control systems.

Air enters the inlet port of the filter and is pushed downwards through a fixed swirl vane which causes a swirling action in the air.

This swirling action throws the larger dirt particles and water droplets onto the inside walls of the filter bowl where they sink to the bottom. This is the quiet zone.

Automatic drain units are an alternative to manual drains. The autodrain is based on a float mechanism which is lifted when the liquid rises. This opens a diaphragm mechanism which discharges the liquid under pressure. Once the liquid has been discharged the float reseats and the cycle is ready to repeat.

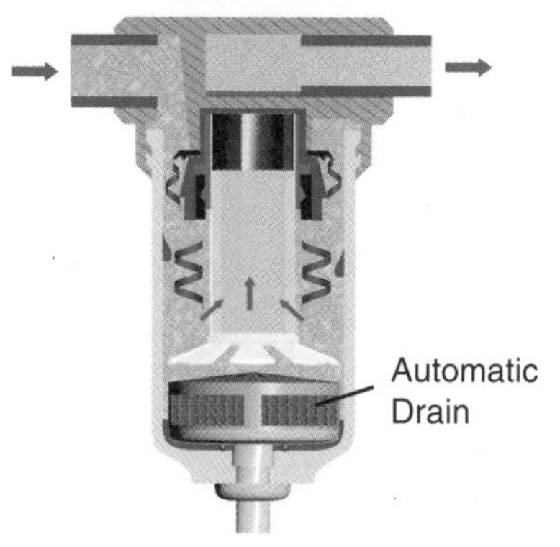

The air then flows through the filter element which can remove particles as small as 5 microns.

The air which exits is now much cleaner.

Different materials can be used as filter elements. All should be checked regularly and cleaned or replaced according to the manufacturer's instructions. The contaminants can be removed by draining the bowl manually or automatically.

The standard filter bowl is made of polycarbonate. If cleaning chemicals which are not compatible with the polycarbonate bowl a metal bowl should be consid-

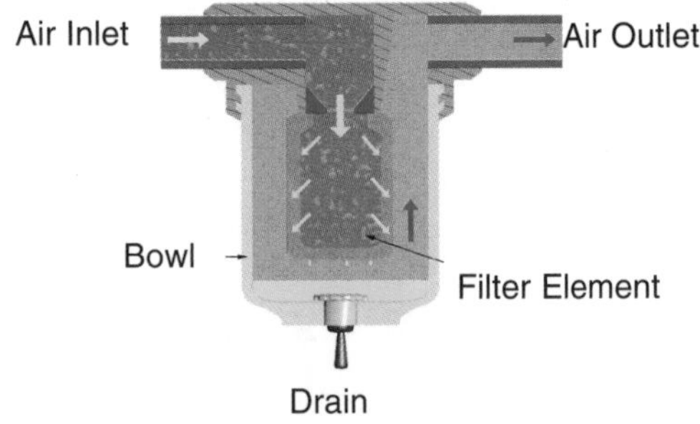

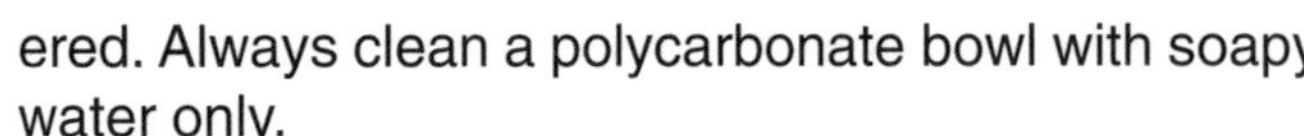
ered. Always clean a polycarbonate bowl with soapy water only.

Some industries including Chemical, Pharmaceutical, Bottling and Packaging, Food Processing and Paint Spraying require oil free air.

Here a **coalescing filter** is used. There are two main differences between a standard and a coalescing filter. First, the flow is reversed, with air flowing into the center of the filter element, then exiting into the system.

Second, the element is disposable and will remove particle contamination down to 0.01 microns. Therefore virtually all oil and water will be removed by this type of filter.

Generally, coalescing filters are expensive due to the nature of the materials used to manufacture the element. Usually borosilicate glass fibres coated with epoxy are used.

Normally a pre-filter is added to increase the element life of the coalescing filter.

Filter Sizing

Air filter sizing is very important and is dependent on two main factors:

- the maximum flow of air used by the equipment
- the maximum pressure drop that can be allowed for the application

If the filter is too small the pressure drop can be very high with the element becoming choked. This results in air starvation.

If the filter is too large the air flow through the unit will be too slow to 'swirl' the air. Therefore heavy contaminants will not be fully removed.

Always check manufacturer's data to ensure the parameters are correct.

Special Filters

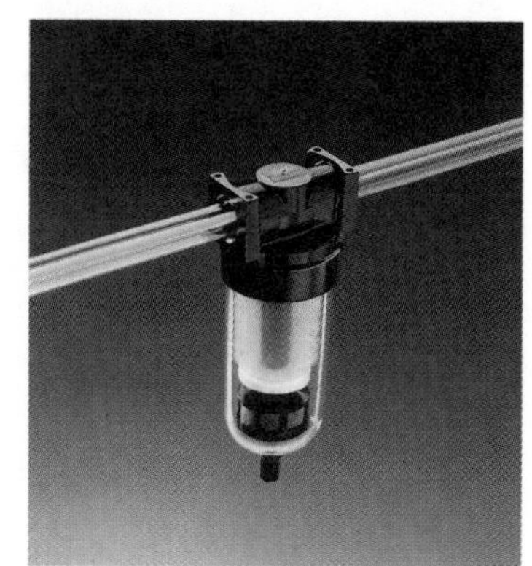

As technology advances, there is a greater requirement for clean, dry, oil free air.

High efficiency filters, if included in a system, will ensure that the air supplied is up to 99.99999% contaminant free. This will increase the life of all pneumatic components, tools and equipment.

This type of filter has elements which are engineered to give maximum performance, and easily and quickly replaced.

Pressure Regulators

Pneumatic systems have an optimum working pressure which is generally lower than the main air supply.

The compressor working pressure should be reduced to the exact requirements of the pneumatic system.

Air pressure fluctuations caused by downstream demands should also be stabilized.

By incorporating a regulator in the circuit the pressure can be adjusted to give the correct cylinder thrust.

Pascal's Law can be used here to determine the correct force. **Force = Area x Pressure**

For an example of this see Module 1, Gas Laws.

In addition, savings are made in the volume of compressed air used and therefore the system is more economical to run. This is because the compressor does not need to operate as often if the system working pressure is lowered.

For example by halving the pressure at the point of use, the volume is almost doubled due to the expansion of the air.

Boyle's Law can be used to calculate the volume available at this lower pressure. **$\text{Pressure}_1 \times \text{Volume}_1 = \text{Pressure}_2 \times \text{Volume}_2 = \text{Constant}$**

For an example of this see Module 1, Gas Laws.

The main regulator types are:

- diaphragm
- piston

Diaphragm Regulator

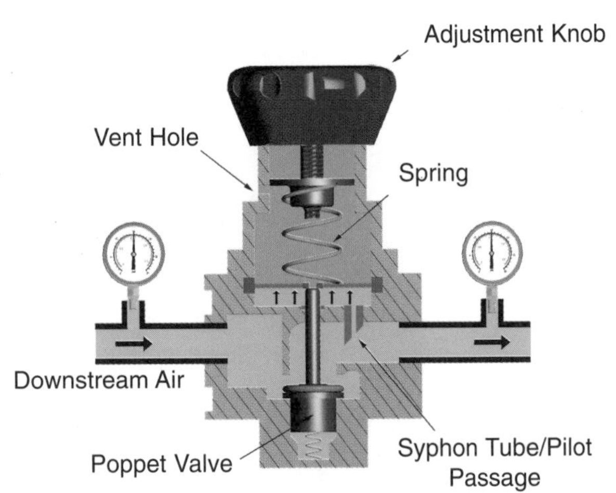

In this type of regulator, pressure fluctuations are sensed by a flexible diaphragm(or moveable piston).

This large control diaphragm is connected to the downstream system air pressure via a pilot passage or siphon tube and the diaphragm works against a spring. When downstream pressure increases, it is sensed via the pilot passage onto the diaphragm. The diaphragm has a spring force set by the adjustment knob which opposes the air pressure.

When the required pressure is reached the diaphragm allows the poppet valve to move, giving a pressure drop through the valve.

As the pressure downstream drops it is sensed by the diaphragm and the poppet valve opens. This adjusts the position of the poppet valve, which limits the downstream pressure to the preset value.

The diaphragm is very sensitive and accurate due to the large surface area. To ensure that the downstream pressure is vented to the atmosphere if it reaches a higher limit than that set by the regulator, the diaphragm has a hole in the center.

As an example if the adjustment knob is screwed counter clockwise, the excess air pressure, due to the reduction in spring force is vented automatically.

When the downstream pressure is higher than the set spring pressure the diaphragm will rise up off the poppet valve opening the vent hole and release excess air pressure to the atmosphere.

When downstream pressure is reduced, the diaphragm reseats on to the poppet stem and pressure regulation resumes. The regulator described is of the 'self bleed' or 'venting' type.

Non-Venting Regulators

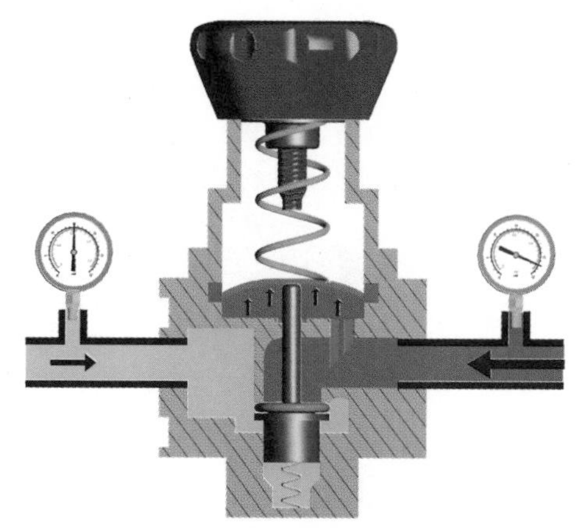

In some cases, where gases other than air are being used, it may be dangerous to allow the gas to vent to the atmosphere.

Here 'non-venting' regulators are used. These do not have the exhaust hole in the valve body or a vent hole in the diaphragm which means that the downstream pressure is locked off and cannot be released until the system is operated.

If the downstream equipment is subject to external forces, the regulator poppet seat closes, allowing the downstream pressure to rise. This may lead to a dangerously high pressure.

Because of this, most industrial compressed air systems use 'venting' pressure regulators.

Piston Regulators

These use a piston in place of a diaphragm to sense the downstream pressure fluctuations. The piston, in turn, works against a set spring pressure. These regulators are very robust.

Lubrication

Most pneumatic equipment needs lubrication to reduce friction on moving parts.

In some vehicles, the oil for the compressor is supplied by the engine lubrication system.

In industrial applications the lubrication is supplied by other means.

Some lubricants such as compressor oils are totally unsuitable for pneumatic components as they can damage seals.

Synthetic compressor oil can affect the integrity of polycarbonate bowls of filters and lubricators. This incompatibility may cause a malfunction and increases the cost of maintenance.

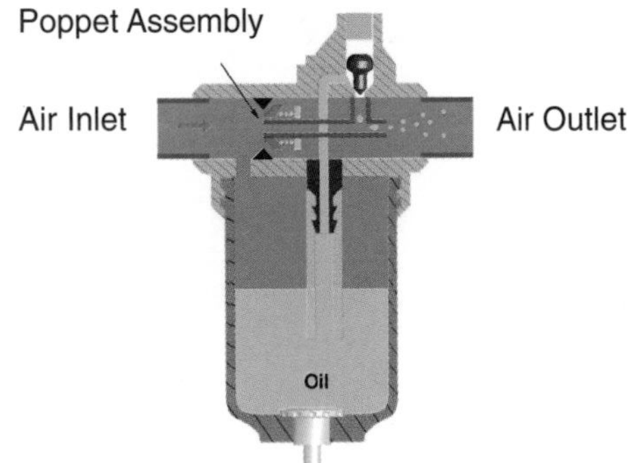

The most common types of lubricators are:

- oil mist lubricator
- micro mist lubricator

In the 'oil mist' lubricator oil is discharged directly into the airline as a fine mist or fog.

It is designed to give a constant density of lubrication.

Any increase in air flow results in a proportional increase in oil mist. The proportional increase in oil mist by an increase in air flow is achieved by the spring loaded poppet assembly.

As the flow increases and the valve opens, the area is increased and a pressure differential created.

This is called the **Venturi effect**.

The air pressure at the oil outlet tube decreases and draws the oil into the system which is then atomized into very small particles or mist. A decrease in air flow reduces the Venturi effect which decreases the amount of oil taken into the system.

To achieve the correct lubrication the lubricator should be no more than 5 metres (16ft) away and above or level with the equipment to be lubricated.

Micro Mist Lubricator

Sometimes known as the recirculating lubricator, the oil particles range from 0.01 micrometers (microns) to 2 micrometers (microns) in diameter. These particles therefore stay in suspension for greater distances allowing longer air lines between the lubricator and the components. Elbows and vertical runs will not wet out (coalesce) the droplets. The larger droplets are returned by recirculating the air flow into the bowl.

Here we see the parts of the micro mist (recirculating) lubricator.

A	=	Venturi section
B	=	Venturi
C	=	Restrictor disc
D	=	Pick up tube
E	=	Check ball
F	=	Metering block assembly
G	=	Metering screw
H	=	Inner and outer sight dome
I	=	Nozzle tube
J	=	Curved baffle plate
K	=	Opening to main line

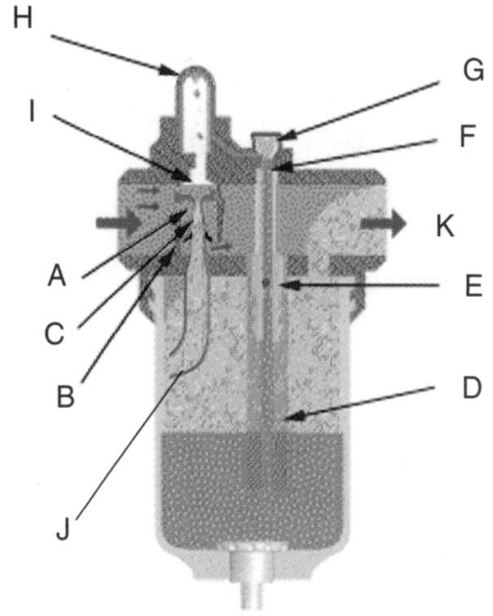

The **micro mist** lubricator works in a similar manner to the oil mist lubricator. However, the atomized oil flows through the curved baffle plate (J) and is deflected against the bowl.

Larger particles of oil coalesce and fall back into the reservoir. The remaining micro mist is carried through the opening (K) which forms and mixes with the air which bypassed the restrictor disc (C).

As air flow increases, the restrictor disc (C) deflects allowing more air to bypass the Venturi (B) in the Venturi section (A).

The pressure drop increases and therefore oil delivery rate also increases in proportion.

The check ball (E) in the pick up tube (D) prevents reverse oil flow when the air flow stops.

Therefore when air flow resumes oil delivery starts almost immediately.

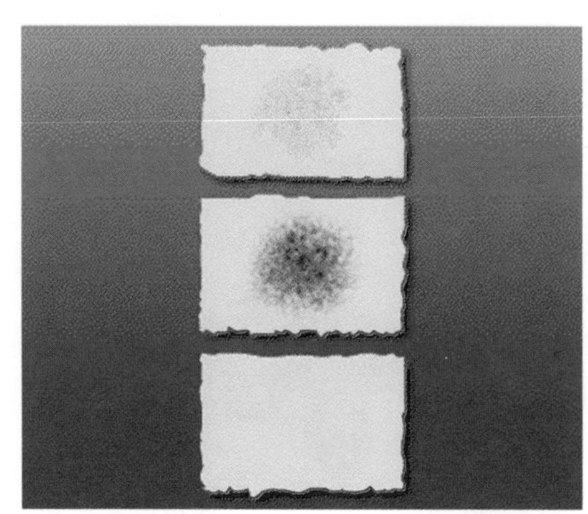

A simple test for correct lubrication is to place a piece of white blotting paper over the exhaust port of a valve and operate the system a few times.

If the lubricator is set correctly, there will be a faint yellow circle on the blotting paper.

Too much oil will saturate the paper. Too small an amount of oil will leave the paper dry.

Filter - Regulator - Lubricator

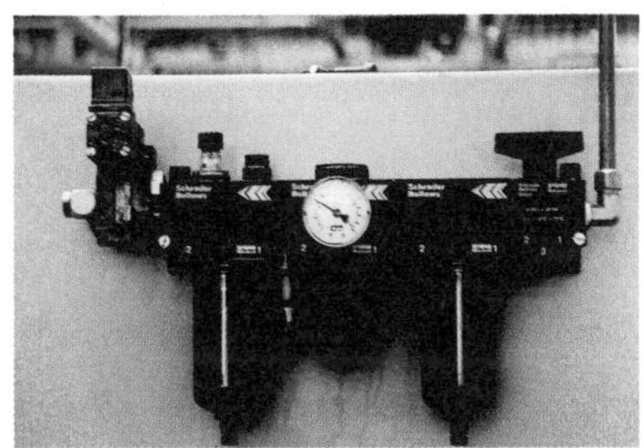

Units can be supplied as a combination unit, an FRL.

They should:

- Be sized correctly for maximum flow and pressure.
- Be easily accessible for service and maintenance.
- Have a self relieving shut off valve or lock out valve upstream to isolate the system.

Remember - FRL's in a system will:

- Remove contamination.
- Give correct pressure to increase system efficiency.
- Reduce wear and extend equipment life with correct lubrication, therefore saving money.
- Reduce pressure fluctuations.

3 Way
Shutoff / lockout
Valve
Regulator
Filter
Lubricator

The arrangement of the FRL's, sometimes called service units is important.

Some service units come complete with a three way shut-off valve, to exhaust the downstream pressure, when closed off.

The filter is always the first unit after the shut-off / lockout valve.

The regulator, which is placed downstream of the filter reduces the pressure supplied to components.

The final item is the lubricator, which is then connected to the system. A quick acting connector may also be attached to the lubricator outlet for ease of system disconnection.

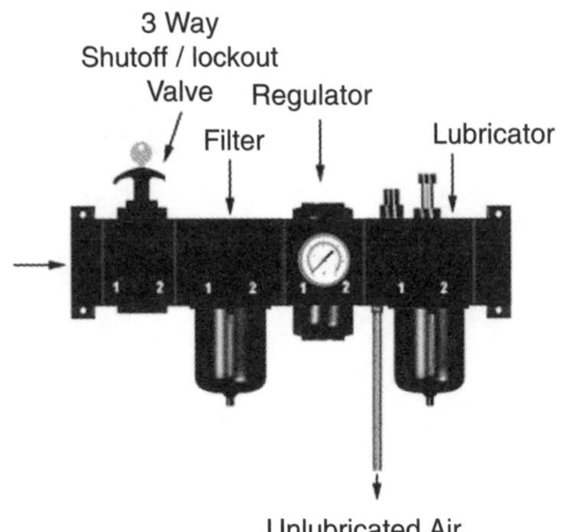

In some sub-systems it is important to have unlubricated air, for example in a paint spraying area.

A line may be connected before the lubricator to supply filtered, regulated but unlubricated air to the sub-system.

Summary

Air Preparation

- Air preparation equipment **cools**, **dries**, **filters**, **regulates** and **lubricates** compressed air.

- Cooling of the air leads to the condensation of moisture which can corrode pipes. The **aftercooler** is generally placed after the compressor to remove some of this moisture.

- A dryer can also be installed to remove moisture where very dry air is required. The three main types are **absorbtion**, **adsorbtion** and **refrigerant** dryers.

Filters

- Filters are placed on the air intake and in the air lines to remove particle contamination.

Regulators

- Regulators control the maximum working pressure within a pneumatic system. These can be '**venting**' or '**non-venting**' types.

Lubricators

- Lubricators supply **oil mist** or **micro mist** lubrication to ensure that there is low friction between moving parts in a pneumatic system.

FRLs

- Filter, regulator and lubricators can be used in various combinations dependent upon the equipment to be serviced.

Air Distribution

Objectives

In this section the following will be examined:

- Plant installation
- Piping and brackets used in mainline, branch and control systems
- Costs and detection of leakage in pneumatic systems

Plant Installation

The compressor must be of sufficient size and capacity to run the system efficiently.

The air inlet filter should be positioned to draw in clean, cool air. This must be maintained and replaced regularly.

In larger compressed air systems, a second standby compressor is usually installed.

This will supply compressed air if the first compressor fails or will 'start up' if demand is high.

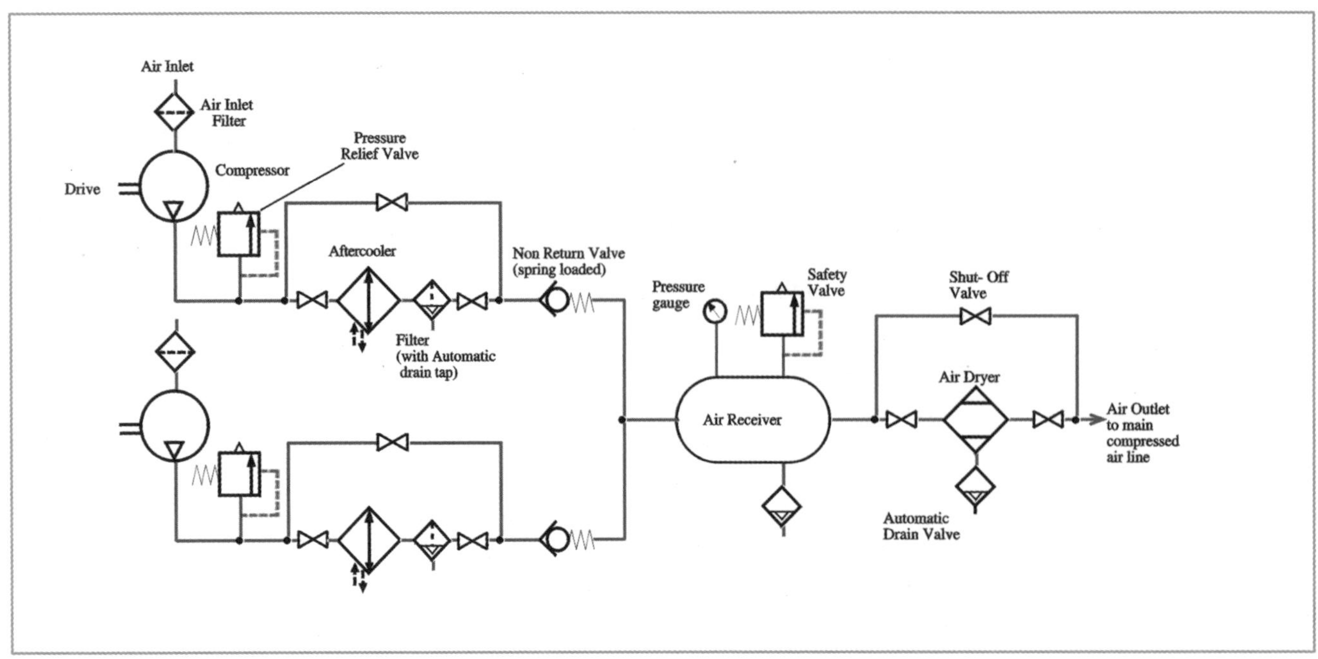

Safety relief valves must be placed between the compressor and stop valves unless these are built into the compressor, The system must always have one to ensure unsafe pressures are not reached.

The aftercooler will remove a certain amount of moisture from the compressed air.

Each compressor line has its own aftercooler with bypass facility for maintenance purposes. If only one aftercooler is used, it must be of sufficient size to cope with the air delivery of both compressors.

Filters with automatic drains are situated downstream of the aftercooler to remove contaminants.

These filters usually have an indicator to show the status of the filter cartridge. Non-return or check valves are important components at this point. They ensure that no pressurized air can get upstream when equipment is being serviced or maintained.

Stop valves may leak and create a danger to personnel by allowing the system to pressurize or if they are not closed due to hurried maintenance or trouble shooting. **Safety procedures must always be followed.**

The air receiver or tank acts as a storage vessel along with other functions. The type and size depends on various factors such as flow, pressure and system demand.

The air receiver should have an automatic drain to remove the condensate, which should be disposed of correctly. Putting this condensate to ground or into a drain is illegal in certain countries.

The air receiver must have a safety relief valve connected directly to it to stop over pressurization and a pressure gauge to record system pressure.

The compressed air dryer is the final item before the compressed air enters the factory system.

Dependent upon the type of dryer used, pre-filters and downstream filters may be incorporated.

The air dryer, dependent on type, may be placed before or after the air receiver; consult the manufacturers data. However, a desiccant dryer, placed downstream of an air receiver is less likely to be contaminated by oil or other liquids.

Pipework - Mainline

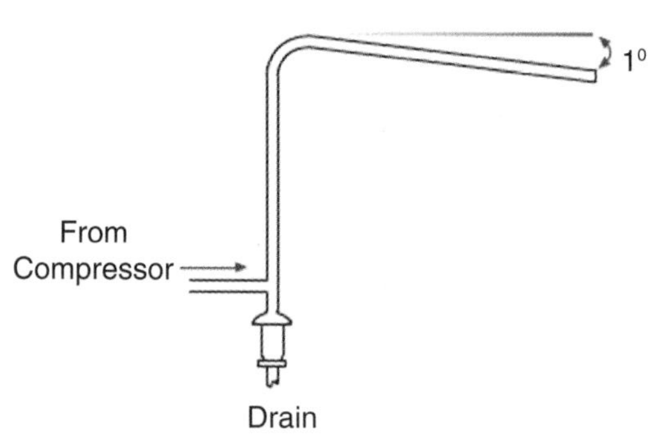

In most factory installations the main air line is installed well above the factory floor.

This prevents the system being damaged by other factory operations, for example, fork lift truck movements.

The system, within a factory, is usually a loop or ring main system, which is the preferred type.

This design minimizes air starvation at points of use furthest from the compressor.

It is important that the loop / ring main is sloped away from the compressor when it is installed.

Sloping the air line prevents any moisture in the pipework from draining back into the compressor plant. That moisture must be removed to prevent corrosion to the pipework.

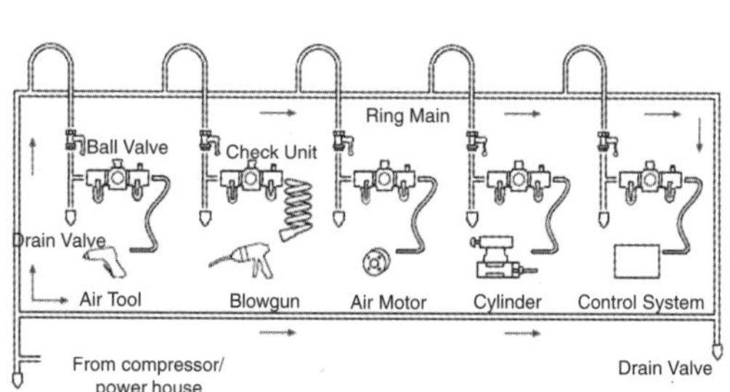

This is achieved by placing **drain** or **drop legs** in the system, where the water can be drawn off.

This can be done manually with just a stop or shutoff valve.

Alternatively, an automatic drain can be installed which opens whenever water is present.

Do not put condensate into a sewer drain as it may be contaminated with oil.

The selection of the pipe bore diameter is important during installation of the main line.

Gauge Pressure		Pipe Bore Size					
Bar	psi	mm	in	mm	in	mm	in
		10	0.4	20	0.8	40	1.56
1.0	14.5	2.8	5.6	7.0	14.0	45	90
4.0	58.0	8.3	16.6	23.0	46.0	135	270
10.0	145.0	19.5	39.0	54.0	108.0	315	630
20.0	290.0	38.0	76.0	105.0	210.0	615	1230
		L\s	cfm	L\s	cfm	L\s	cfm

Pipe manufactures will give, in the data sheet, the maximum flow and pressure permissible for certain diameters. However, the bore chosen should not only be able to carry the existing required flow rates, but also the higher flow rates required if the factory operations were expanded.

If higher air flows were required due to factory development, the entire loop/ring main may need to be replaced, if no expansion criteria was involved at the original design stage. Always use the minimum amount of fittings and keep bend radii as large as practicable to reduce friction.

Branch Line

All branch lines, or **drop legs**, to service machines, hand tools etc. should be taken from the **top** of the main line and dropped down using long sweep bends.

This prevents any condensed moisture in the ring main from draining down to the equipment.

However, these drop legs will require their own drain points to draw off any moisture that condenses in the branch line.

These are normally placed at the bottom of the drop legs. They can be automatic or just manual drains with stop valves.

It is required by law to fit a '**lock out**' valve in the USA, to isolate the system. This is also advisable in all countries for safety reasons.

The valve should have an exhaust to atmosphere in the closed position to vent the system downstream and make it safe for maintenance purposes.

Alternatively a quick coupler or check unit can be fitted. This blocks the air flow when the machine connection is removed.

Beware of exhausting air from the released connection. If a stop valve is not fitted before a quick coupling air may rush out of the open end of the male unit when the hose is disconnected, causing the hose to whip. This would be a safety hazard.

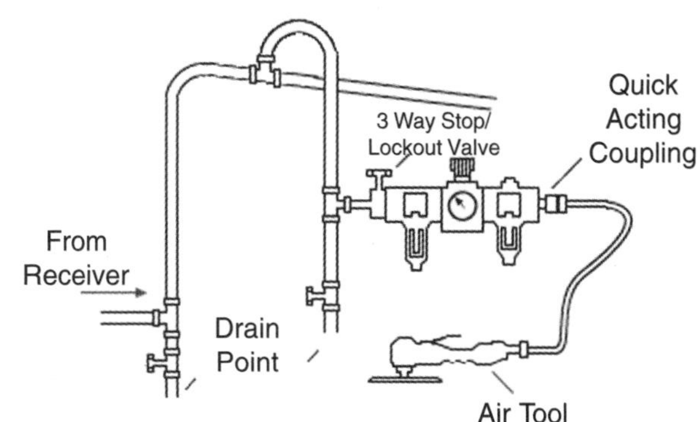

Control Systems

The type and size of piping required in control systems within a machine will depend on the air flow required and the environment that the equipment operates under.

The type is generally specified in the circuit diagram.

The most common types used to connect valves and actuators are:

- copper
- tubing hose
- nylon
- polyurethane

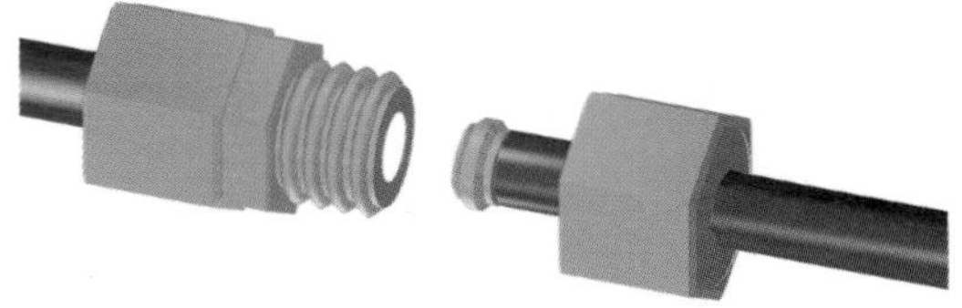

These materials are flexible, easy to handle and easy to connect to fittings.

The two main types of fitting are:

- Compression.
- Push-In.

The compression fitting uses a **ferrule** or **sleeve** that slides onto the pipe.
By tightening the nut onto the body the ferrule is formed over the tube, biting into it to form a positive seal.

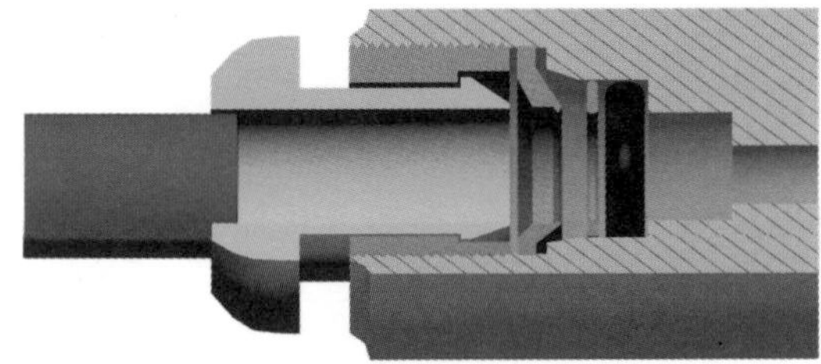

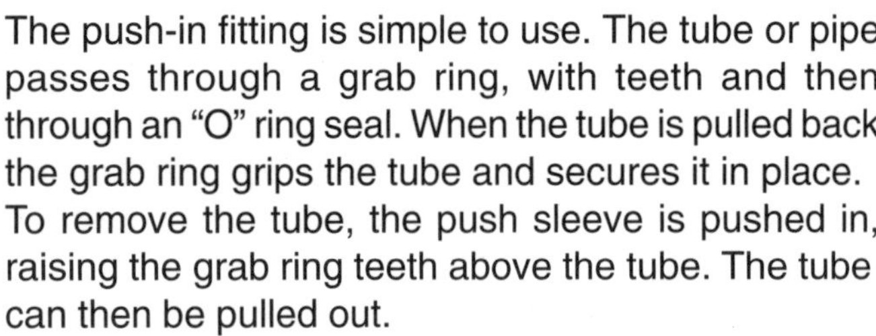

The push-in fitting is simple to use. The tube or pipe passes through a grab ring, with teeth and then through an "O" ring seal. When the tube is pulled back the grab ring grips the tube and secures it in place. To remove the tube, the push sleeve is pushed in, raising the grab ring teeth above the tube. The tube can then be pulled out.

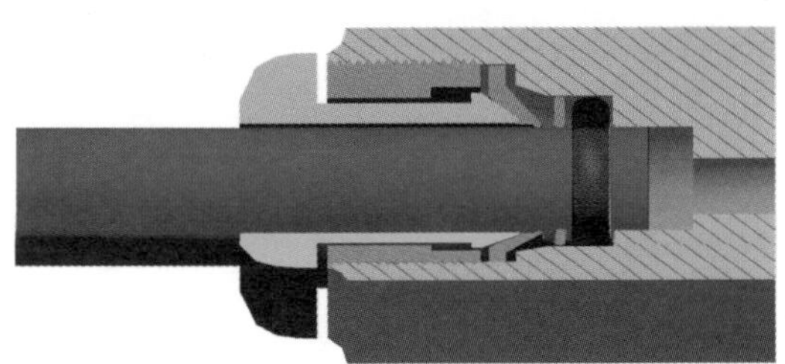

The advantage of a grab ring is that it allows the tube to swivel within the fitting.

Remember:

With these and all other types of fittings you must ensure that all the air has been exhausted before removal and that connection is air tight.

Bracketing / Supports

Intervals Between Pipe Runs			
Pipe size Nom. Bore		Max Intervals for horizontal runs	
mm	ins	m	ins
8	0.32	1.0	39.4
10	0.38	1.0	39.4
15	0.59	1.25	49.25
20	0.79	1.75	68.96
25	0.99	1.75	68.96
32	1.26	2.50	98.5
40	1.58	2.50	98.5
50	1.97	2.75	108.35
65	2.56	3.00	118.2
100	3.94	3.50	137.9
150	5.91	3.50	137.9

Bracketing and supporting of compressed air pipelines is very important as they secure the pipe to the wall, girder, or machine and in the event of a pipe break, will prevent the pipe or tube whipping out of control.

Brackets / supports on main and branch lines should not grip the pipe tightly.

Too tight a grip will not allow for expansion if the pipe is working in a warm or hot environment.

The table on the left gives suggested maximum intervals for horizontal runs for a given pipe size.

Control system brackets / supports with indicators in machine tools serves three functions:

- They 'tidy' up tube runs.
- It is also easier for the engineer to trace a pipe line.
- The indicator shows whether pressure is in the pipeline or not.

Leakage

Water and oil leaks are visible and messy. Gas leaks can be smelt while electrical faults will blow a fuse.

Compressed air leaks, through faulty pipe joints or non-maintained systems, can also be easily detected, usually by the noise they make. While they are easily heard they are often ignored.

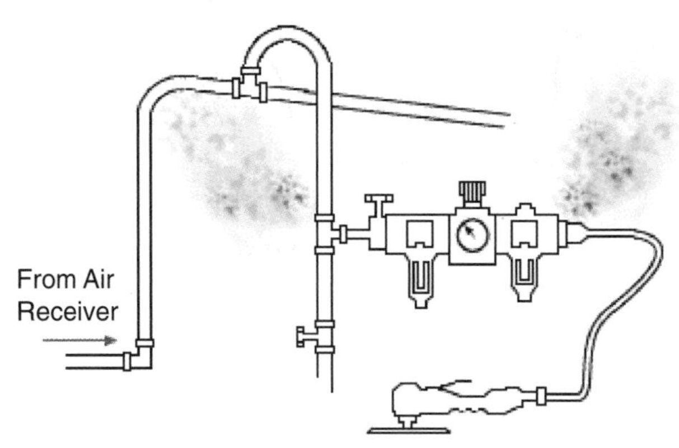

Air leaks may drastically reduce air tool efficiency by lowering both pressure and flow.

A drop of 0.7 bar / 10 psi can result in a reduction of air tool efficiency of 15%.

Air leaks can be more costly than all the other services leakage put together.

Over a period of 1 year this can cost a considerable amount of money.

Hole Diameter		Air Leakageat 7 bar		Power Required by the Compressor	
mm	inch *	L/s	cfm *	Kw	hp *
1	3/64	0.8	1.6	0.24	0.32
2	3/32	3.1	6.2	0.93	1.25
6	1/4	28.2	56.4	8.5	11.40
10	3/8	78.0	150.0	23.4	31

* = Approx

The table on the right shows the electrical power required by a compressor to maintain different leakage rates of air.

For example, a factory with total leaks adding up to 10mm (3/8') bore, loses 78 L/s (150 scfm) at 7 bar (100 psi) and requires 23.4 kw (31hp) of electrical power.

The major cost of leakage is the electrical input to keep the compressor running to make up air losses. This also means more compressor maintenance will be required and its life will be reduced.

Leakage from a compressed air system is not only wasteful but can be dangerous. It is also a noise hazard.

Care should be taken when attempting to trace leaks. **Never** trace a leak by placing your hand or finger over the pipeline.

Air in the bloodstream can lead to loss of a limb or could even be fatal. To trace a leak there are various methods that can be used:

- Soapy water mixture painted onto the suspected area.
- By using a leak detector spray
- Or using an ultrasonic leak detector which is safe and easy to operate.

Summary

- Piping of non corrosive material or A.B.S plastic, carries the air to its point of use
- The main line is normally a loop/ring main and is sited well above the factory floor for protection.
- Main lines should be sloped away from the compressor plant.
- Drain legs are incorporated to remove moisture.
- All branch lines should be taken from the top of the main. A **'lock out'** should be incorporated in the branch line for safety.
- Control system piping is commonly made of nylon, polyurethane or hose.
- The two main types of fittings are **compression** and **push-in** fittings.
- Bracketing / Supporting of pipelines and tubing will keep it secure and prevent it from whipping out of control.
- Hands or fingers should never be used to trace a compressed air leak.

Safe use of Compressed Air

Safety Procedures

There is no greater risk with compressed air than with any other industrial power source such as hydraulic or electrical systems, as long as it is treated with respect.

Compressed air has an extremely high safety record.

Health and Safety considerations must be followed and applied at all times.

Extreme caution must be taken when compressed air is used to clean equipment to prevent particles being blown around. Eye protection is essential.

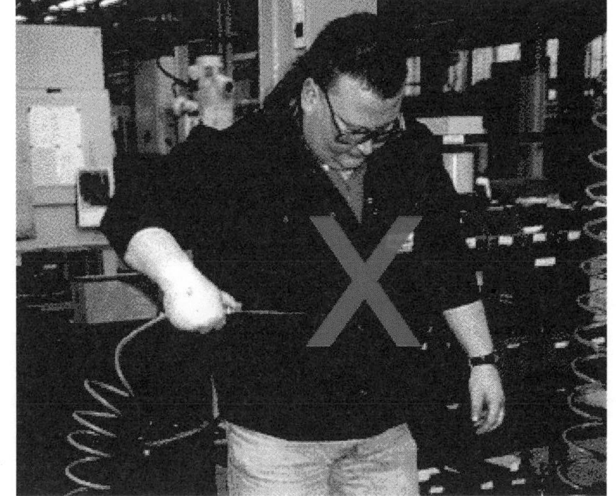

Compressed air must never be applied to the skin, even at low pressures, or directly at a person, or indirectly to clean dirt from clothing.

Air in the blood stream can cause the loss of a limb or may even be fatal.

Compressed air systems are designed to operate at predetermined pressure levels. These levels must never be exceeded.

Never disconnect a hose, piping or fitting until the upstream isolation valve has been shut off, locked out and the air pressure released. All piping must be securely supported before compressed air is passed through it.

This means that damaged piping will not whip, thereby causing injury to personnel or damage to equipment. To prevent injury due to hose failure, regular inspection for cuts, abrasions and deterioration must be undertaken.

Plastic piping must be kept out of direct sunlight and away from heat.

It is essential that all air receivers / tanks comply with **National**, **International** and **Local** standards and must include inspections and tests at regular intervals.

Where compressors are used in parallel or connected to an existing air supply line, a safety device in the form of a non-return valve and / or shut-off, lockout valve should be incorporated in the compressor delivery line.

"NEVER use compressed air directly for breathing purposes." Special filters and regulators are required and come under strict safety regulations.

Before you use a system make sure you know where to find the normal and emergency stopping devices.

Make sure all pressure in the system is released before removing or repairing equipment.

Ensure that removal of air pressure does not make any part of the system unsafe i.e. suspended loads moving.

Check for locked pressure by reading on a pressure gauge or by carefully slackening a fitting to release the air.

DO NOT remove the fitting until all the air has exhausted.

If any electrical or mechanical adjustments have to be made, make sure that these are done by authorized personnel.

You should not attempt to repair a system unless you are authorized to do so.

Once a fault has been rectified thoroughly test the equipment before returning it to operation.

Make sure you know who to talk to if there are any problems.

Noise

Compressed air systems produce noise from various sources. Noise pollution is at the least a nuisance, as it:

- disturbs personnel
- reduces their effective productivity
- can damage health
- is a safety hazard

The compressor(s) with its support equipment requires thoughtful positioning, preferably in its own ventilated enclosure to reduce noise.

This enclosure should be positioned away from the main working area to further reduce noise.

In pneumatic control systems, valve and cylinder action may generate high intensity sound energy with unmuffled exhausting air.

This could lead to hearing loss.

Air noise can also block out a warning signal which could lead to an accident.

Silencers, sometimes called mufflers, are used to reduce exhaust noise.

An efficient silencer should:

- Have low resistance to flow
- Provide sound attenuation
- Be corrosion resistant

Summary

- Safety procedures and codes of practice must be adopted to minimize the risks to health and safety posed by pneumatic systems
- Attention should be paid to minimize noise pollution created by compressed air equipment and exhausting air which may pose a threat to health and safety.

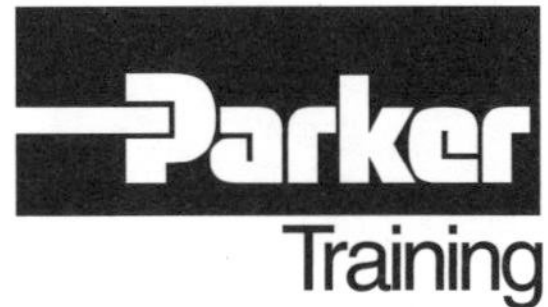

Module 3

Introduction to Pneumatic Equipment

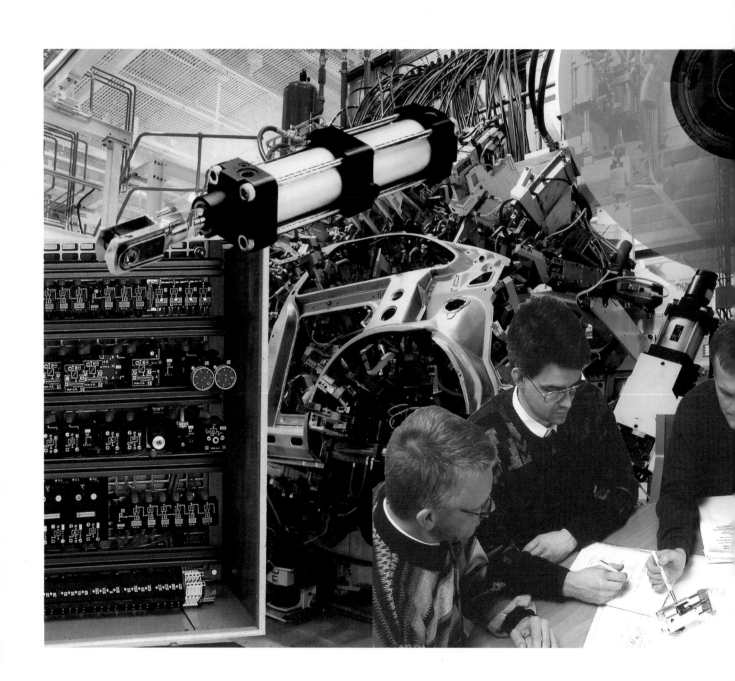

Contents

Valves

Objectives

In this section the following will be examined:

- the importance of valves in pneumatic circuits
- the design, function and port numbering of directional control valves
- methods of operating valves
- the design and function of flow control valves
- the design and function of accessory valves and equipment.

Valve Types

A directional control valve has a number of threaded ports which are connected via internal elements which move within the valve body. They control the direction of air flow through the valve.

These elements are also used to block the passage of air or to allow air to flow.

Valves can be either in-line or sub-base mounted. Sub-based mounted valves can be 'grouped' together on manifolds. They are easier to remove from a control system than in-line valves.

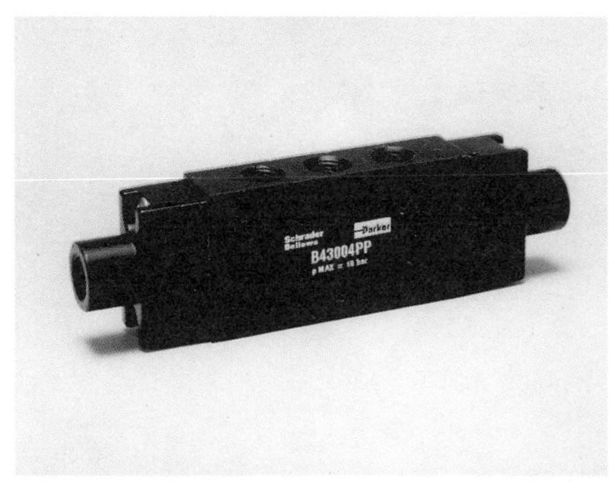

To remove in-lines valves the piping has to be disconnected from the valve ports.

The basic moveable elements of a directional control valve are:

- spool
- poppet

Spool valves

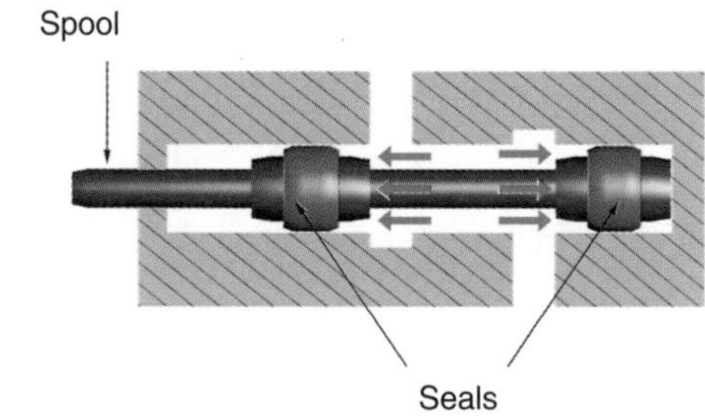

The spool type operates by moving a spool within the valve body. This allows the valve ports to be connected or blocked.

There are various sealing mechanisms used to prevent leakage in pneumatic valves. The type and cost varies. The type of seal and moveable element used can be determined by referring to manufacturer's data sheets.

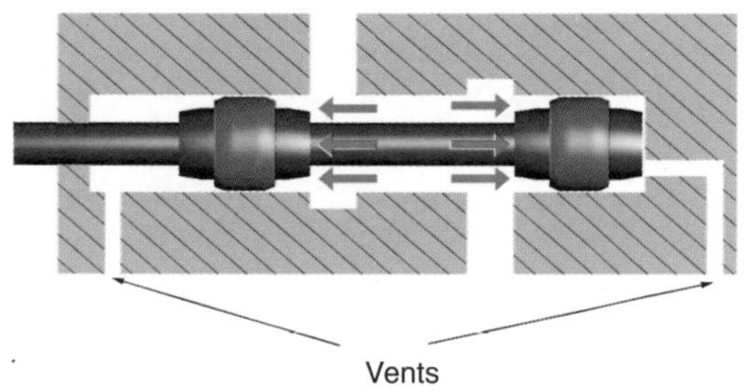

These moveable elements (spools) are said to be '**Balanced**'. They are constructed so that the forces inside the valve counter one another.

The compressed air pressure in the valve works against the area of the spool lands which are equal in area, thus giving an equal force or 'balance'.

Such 'balance' is crucial as it avoids any unnecessary internal pressure that could affect the operation of the valve or other system components.

Some directional control valves also incorporate exhaust vents to prevent air pressure building up behind the spools. Such a build up could lock the valve spool in a fixed position.

Poppet Valve

The main characteristics of poppet valves are:

- Rapid cycling
- Small travel for maximum flow
- Minimum wear
- Long service life
- Positive shut off
- Self cleaning
- Minimal maintenance
- Non-lubricated service
- Large flow capabilities

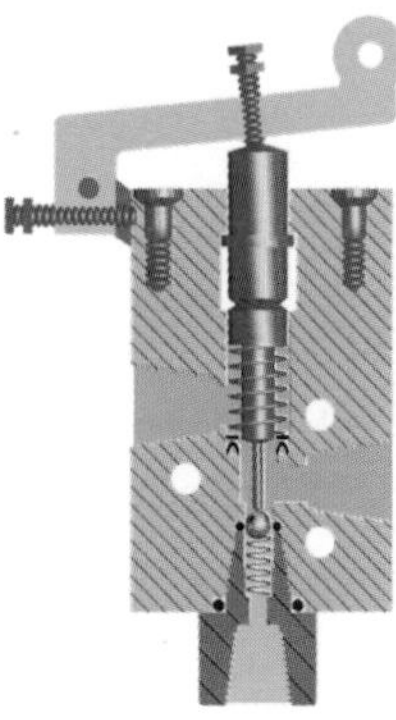

The poppet valve operates by moving a poppet assembly against a seat.

This forms a positive seal and allows the valve ports to be connected or blocked.

Valve Port Numbering

Main Line Input Port	1
Output Ports	2,4,6 etc
Exhaust Ports	3,5,7 etc
Pilot Ports	10,12,14 etc
The Input Symbol	or
The Exhaust Symbol	or
	Threaded Port / Exhaust Vent

Valve ports are numbered under **ISO 5599**.

The main or input port is '1'. The output ports are '4' and '2'. The exhaust ports are '5' and '3'. Pilot ports are '10', '12' and '14'.

Fig 1. Shows two valves showing the labels with the port numbering.

The symbol here represents a double pilot 3/2 directional control valve. When an air signal is placed on pilot port '12', air flows from port '1' to '2'.

When an air signal is placed on port '10' the main supply is blocked, e.g.. '1' to '0'.

Under **ISO 1219** standards the 3/2 valve symbol can be drawn in two different ways as shown here giving the same operational function. Both symbols are used in this program.

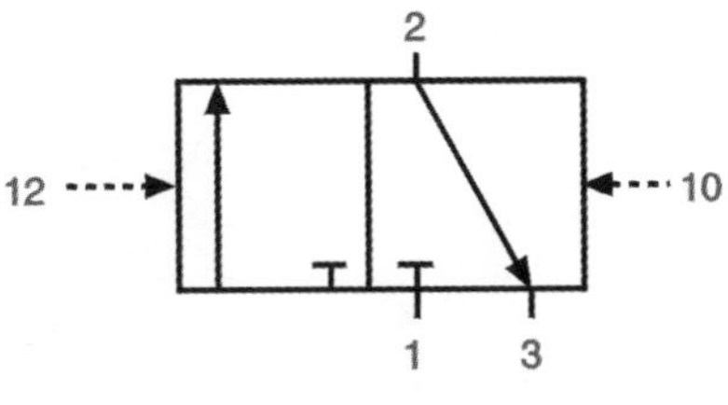

Fig.1

or

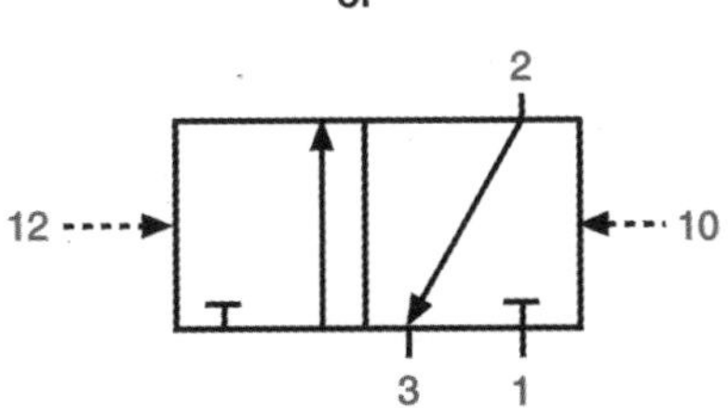

Fig 2. Represents a double pilot 4/2 directional control valve.

A signal to pilot port '12' directs air from port '1' to port '2'.

A signal to pilot port '14' directs air from port '1' to port '4'.

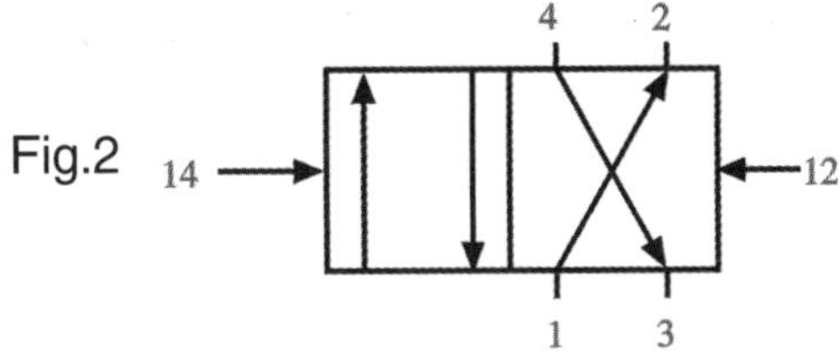

Fig.2

Fig 3. Represents a double pilot 5/2 valve.

This valve has an extra exhaust port '5'.

When a signal is placed on port '12', air flows from port '1' to '2'.

The air at port '4' exhausts through port '5'.

When a signal is placed on port '14', air flows from port '1' to port '4'.

The air at port '2' exhausts through port '3'.

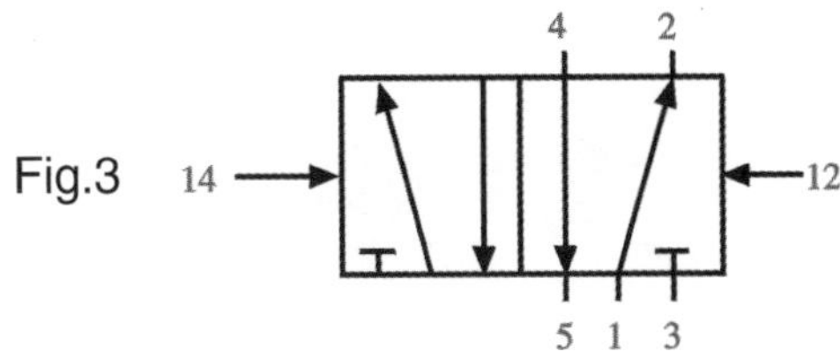

Fig.3

Fig 4. Represents a double pilot 5/3 valve.

This valve has a center position with all ports closed.

When a pilot signal is placed on port '12' air flows from port '1' to port '2'.

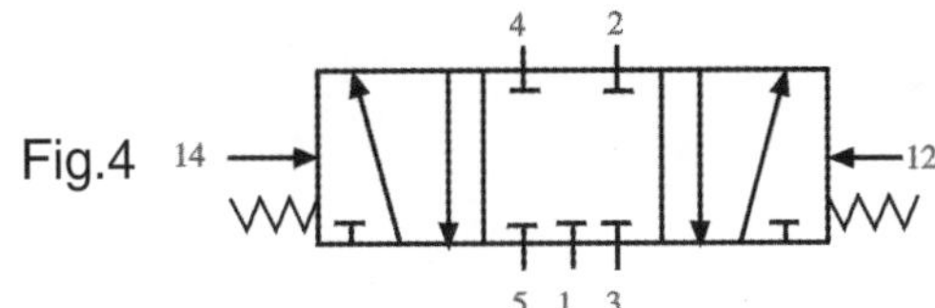

Fig.4

When a pilot signal is placed on port '14' air flows from port '1' to '4'.

The center position is achieved by spring actuators when no pilot signals are present.

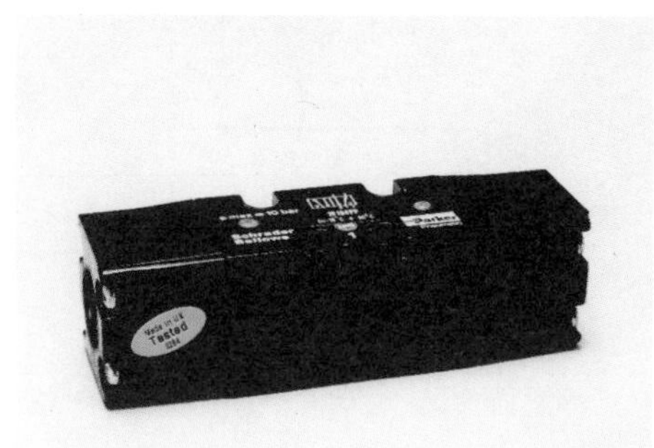

Directional Control Valves

Directional control valves usually have reference numbers applied to them such as:

- 2/2
- 3/2
- 4/2
- 5/2
- 5/3

In this section these are explained.

2/2 Valve

The first number in the 2/2 designation refers to the number of ports in the valve. Thus a 2/2 valve has two ports, an 'in' and an 'out' port.

The second number in the designation refers to the number of positions the valve element can take. In this case, it is 2.

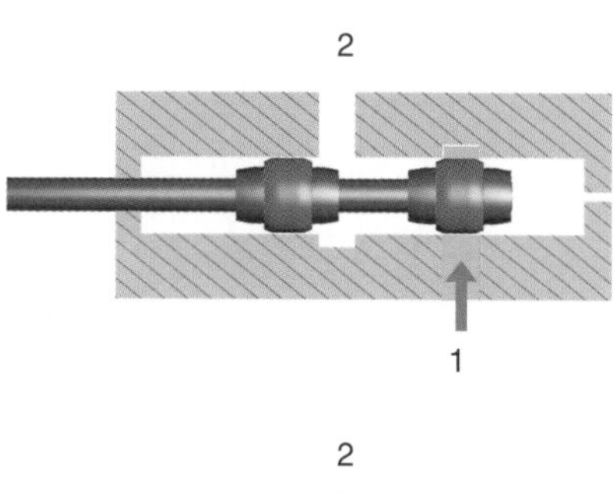

These valves are often used in pneumatic circuits either to open (passing), or to close a path (non passing), for flow in a single line.

The working / outlet port is referenced by the number '2', and the pressure / inlet by the number '1'.

In this position, the sliding spool blocks the flow path between ports '1' and '2'.

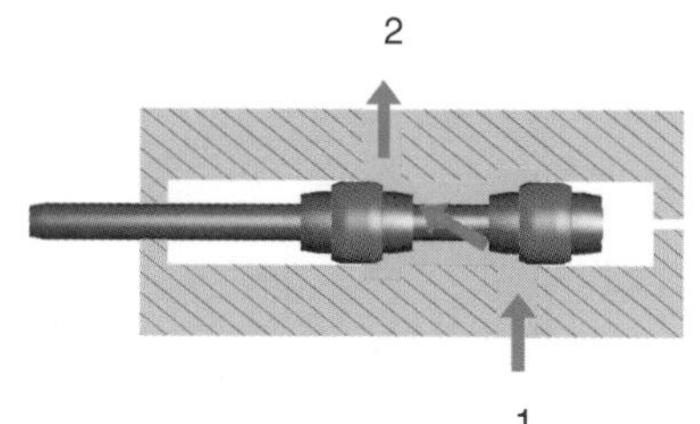

The valve is closed (non passing).

By sliding the spool to the right, we can open the flow path between ports '1' and '2'.

In this position, the valve is open (passing) air flow through it. These valves are used as "start stop valves".

3/2 Valve - Spool Type Normally Closed/ Non Passing

The 3/2 valve has three ports and two positions. It differs from the 2/2 valve in having the extra port which usually acts as an exhaust port open to the atmosphere.

These valves are used as 'start valves', 'limit valves' or 'proof of position valves'.

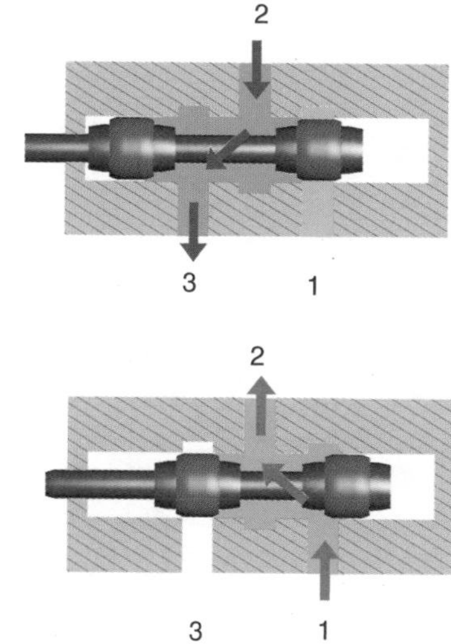

In this position, flow between the supply pressure port, 1, and the actuator / outlet port '2' is blocked, i.e. the valve is closed or non passing.

In this position the valve is open or passing, with air flowing from the supply port, '1', to the actuator / outlet port '2'.

Returning the valve to its original / neutral, or at rest position closes off the air supply '1' to the outlet port '2'.

Air from the outlet port '2' is vented to the atmosphere via the exhaust port '3'.

The 3/2 valve just described is a non-passing valve. Here, the flow path to the actuator is blocked until the valve is switched or activated.

3/2 Valve - Spool Type Normally Open Passing

In the normally passing valve, the flow path to the actuator is **open (passing)** until the valve is switched.

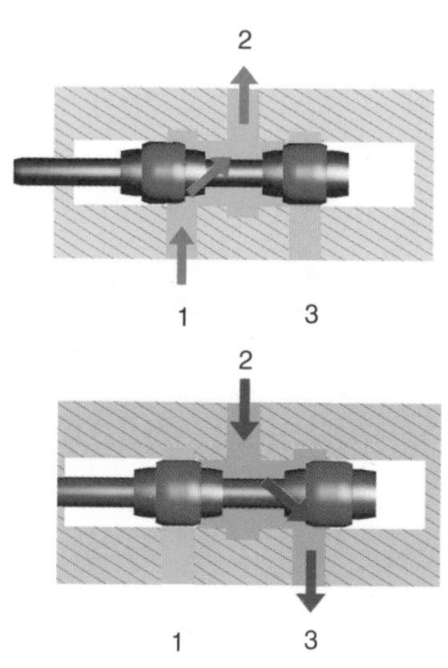

In this position, air can flow from the supply port '1' to the actuator / output port '2'. Flow to the exhaust port '3' is prevented.

By sliding the spool to the right, we can block the flow between ports '1' and '2'.

At the same time, the path between ports '2' and '3' is open or passing.

3/2 Poppet Valve

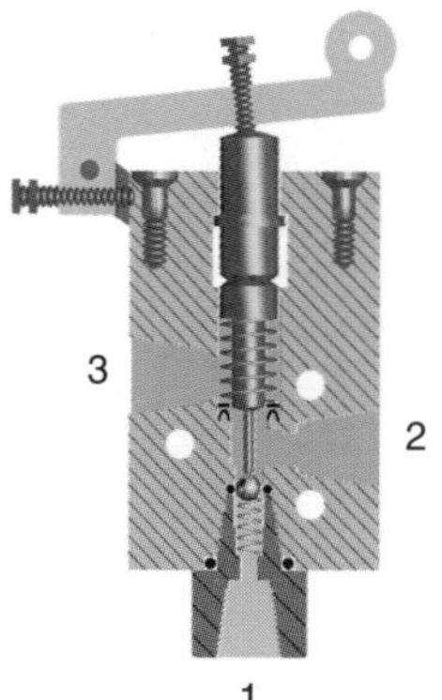

The 3/2 poppet valve is generally used as a signal valve or limit valve.

The poppet valve shown here is a 3/2 normally closed/ non passing type.

Inlet port '1' is closed (blocked) and outlet port '2' is open (passing) to exhaust port '3'.

When the valve is actuated the exhaust port closes (non passing) before the inlet port opens (passing) to the outlet port.

4/2 Valve

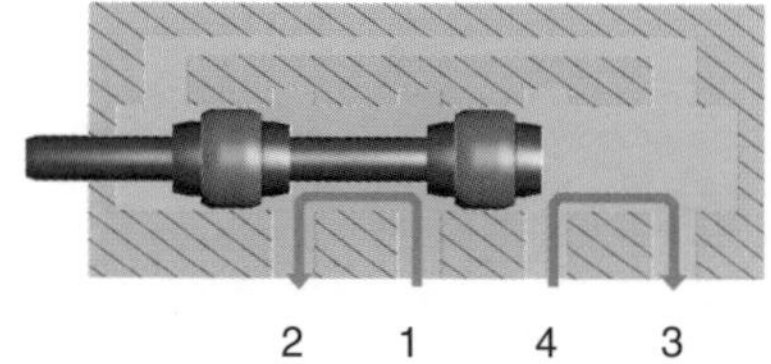

The 4/2 valve has four ports and two positions. It has two working lines / output ports '4' and '2', a main or supply port '1' and an exhaust port '3'.

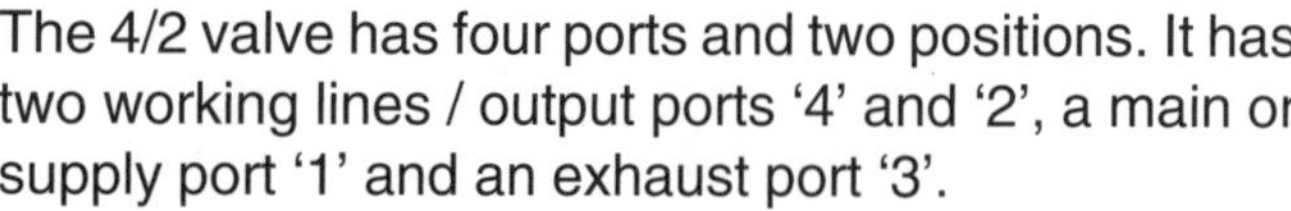

These valves are normally used in circuits in conjunction with double acting cylinders.

In this position air can flow from the supply port, '1', to output port '2'.

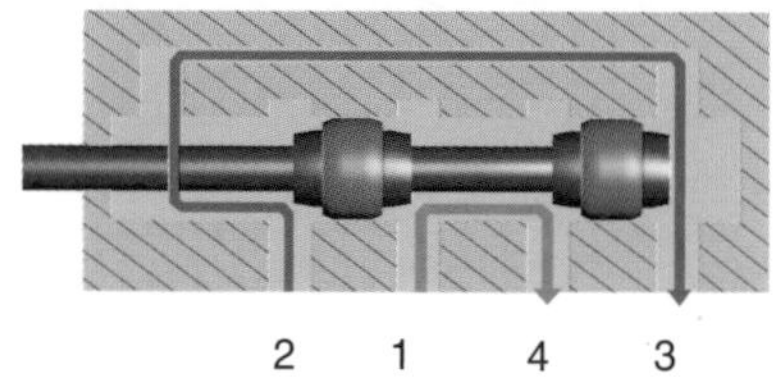

Simultaneously, air flows from the other output port, '4', to the exhaust port, '3'.

By sliding the spool to the right, we can redirect the air flow from supply port '1' to output port '4'.

5/2 Valve

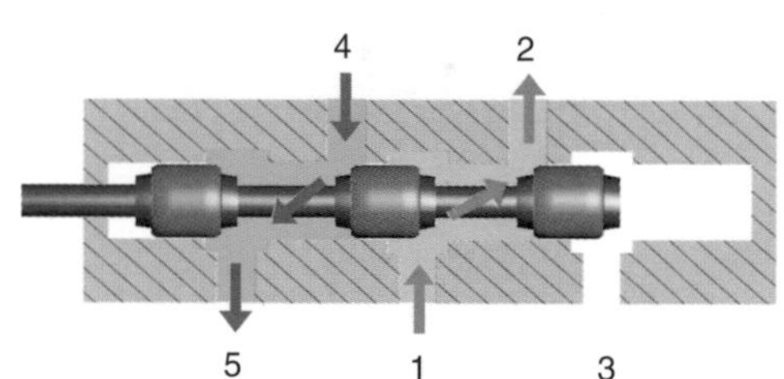

A 5/2 valve has five ports and two positions. It differs from the 4/2 valve in that it has an additional exhaust port, usually labelled '5'.

In this position, air is supplied via the supply port '1', to actuator / output port '2'.

At the same time air exhausts from actuator / output port '4' to exhaust port '5'.

Exhaust port '3' is blocked.

By sliding the spool to the right we can redirect the flows.

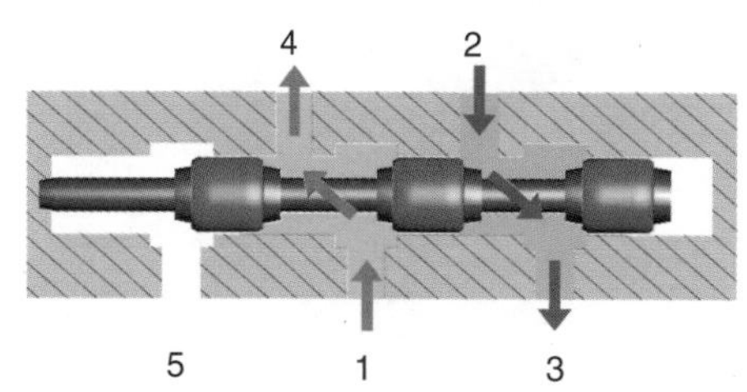

In this position air is supplied from the supply port '1' to actuator / output port '4'. At the same time air exhausts from actuator / output port '2' to exhaust port '3'.

Exhaust port '5' is now blocked. The 4/2 and 5/2 valves are the most common types of directional control valves used to operate double acting pneumatic cylinders.

5/3 Valve

This valve is a version of the 5/2 valve with an additional third or middle position.

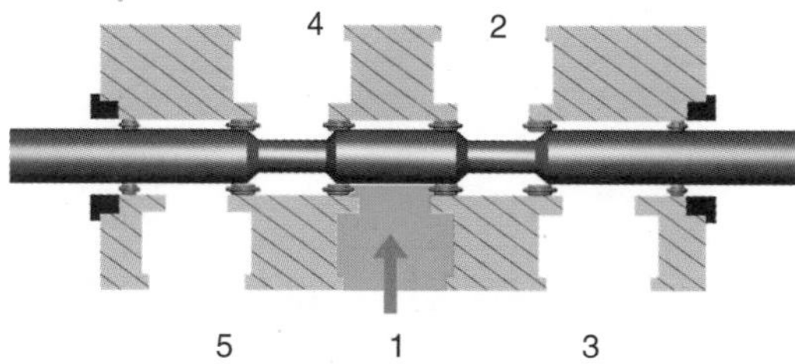

Usually, its center position is called the neutral position.

Many combinations of these valves are available and are used in many applications.

Main air supply is to port '1'. Ports '2' and '4' are the actuator / output ports. '3' and '5' are the exhaust ports. In this neutral position all ports are blocked.

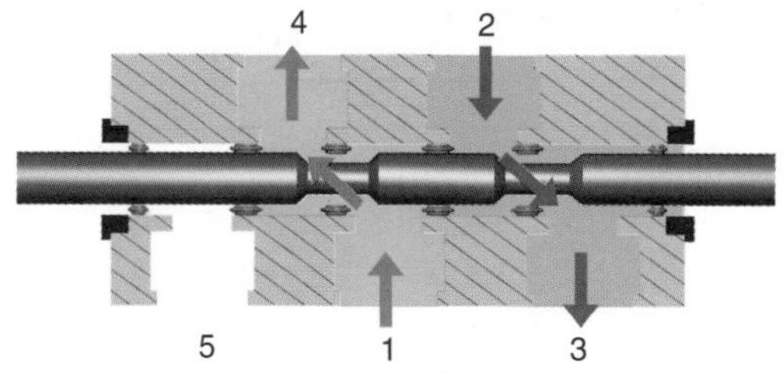

By sliding the spool to the right, air flows from port '1' to port '4'.

Air from port '2' is exhausted via port '3'.

By the sliding the spool to the left air flow goes from port '1' to port '2' while the air from port '4' is exhausted via port '5'.

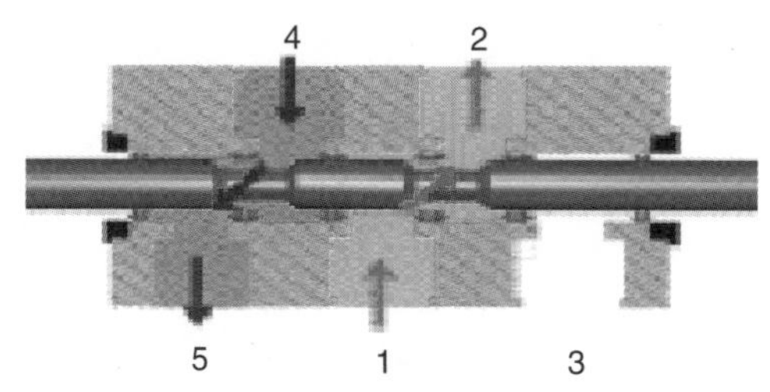

The mid-position is achieved by various mechanisms such as spring centering or via detent.

Valve actuator types

All valves require some form of actuator to actuate or move the spool or poppet to each working position.

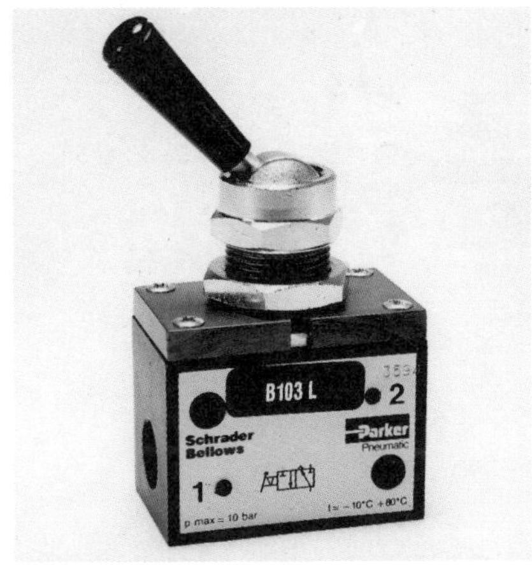

These range from spring type actuators, which ensure the valve always returns to the initial position, to electrical solenoid valves that can operate from sophisticated electronic control systems on fully automatic machines.

Opposite is shown a lever actuator.

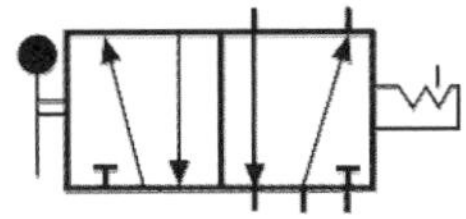

It is operated by hand to make the valve move to its working position.

A spring returns the valve, automatically, back to its original position, whenever the lever is released. If the spring is replaced by a 'detent' symbol, the valve does not return to its original position when the lever is released.

Instead, the operator must reverse the lever movement to return the valve to its original position.

Other forms of manual control of valves include:

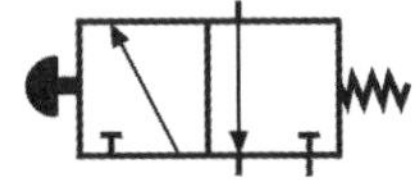

- Push button control

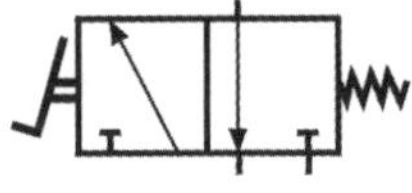

- Foot pedal control

In a number of circuits it may not be practical for valves to be controlled manually. For example, the valve may be inaccessible. In this case, the valve can be controlled remotely. This can be done electrically, using a **Solenoid** valve.

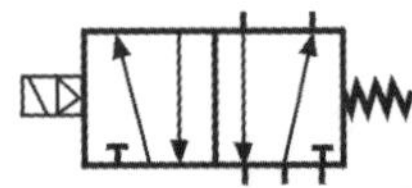

Here is the symbol for a solenoid valve. It is returned to its initial or non-actuated position by a spring.

When the solenoid is energized air is supplied to a pilot operator to actuate the valve.

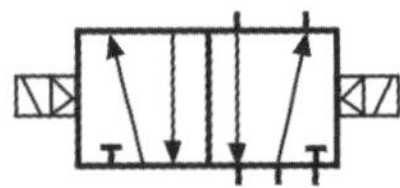

The symbol here is for a solenoid valve where the return to the original position is also by solenoid actuator.

To reduce solenoid size and electrical power the valve is changed over (shifted) with an air pilot.

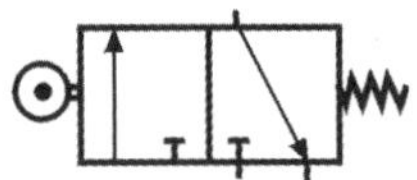

Here a roller actuates the valve. The valve is activated by a cam or component operating the roller.

The actuators on this valve are operated by compressed air which can be supplied by other valves or equipment in the system.

The actuator is known as a 'Pilot'.

Flow Control Valves

Flow control or restrictor valves are widely used in pneumatic systems to slow down actuators when required.

Normally this is done by restricting the air leaving the actuator.

Flow control valves vary in both type and size. Selection of a particular type is determined by its application within the circuit.

The most common types of flow control valves and their construction are highlighted next.

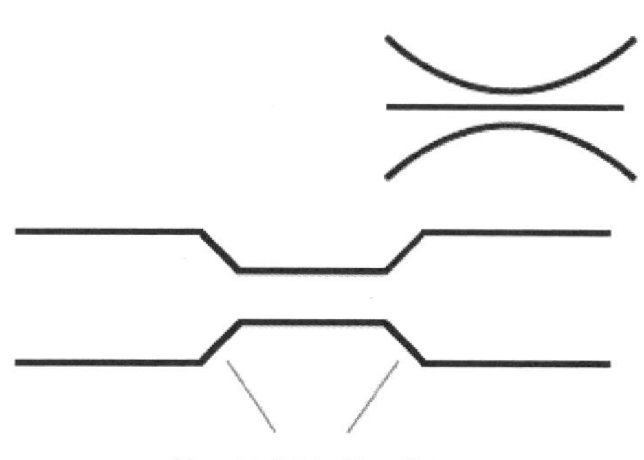
Non-Variable Restrictor

Non Variable Restrictor

The simplest method of flow control is to insert a fixed orifice or restrictor in the air line. This would be a pipe of a smaller bore diameter or a fitting with a small hole drilled in it.

However this restriction is non-adjustable and so provides a fixed air flow.

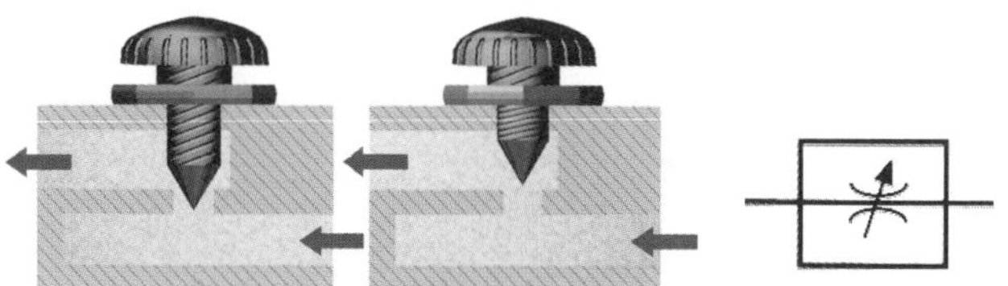

Variable Restrictor

Here the level of restriction can be changed by turning a screw to increase or decrease the orifice size.

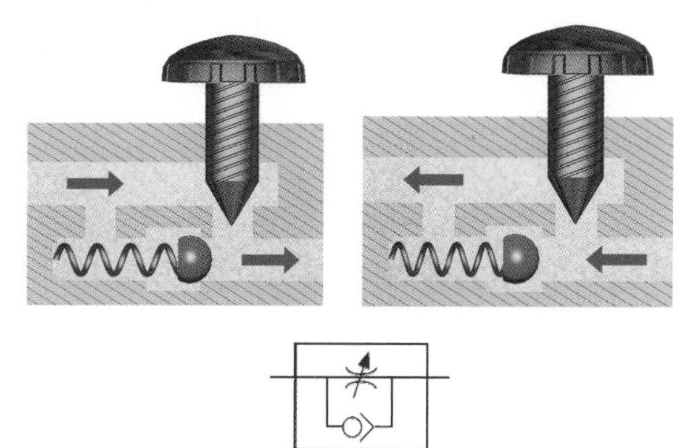

Flow Control Valve With Bypass

In certain applications restriction of air flow will be required in one direction only.

To achieve this a **check** or **non-return** valve is placed in parallel with the orifice. This blocks the flow of air in one direction, forcing the air to pass through the orifice.

However, air can flow, unrestricted, in the opposite direction, as the poppet is forced off its seat by the reverse air flow.

This type of valve can be used where an actuator has a slow working stroke but a fast return stroke.

Shuttle Valve

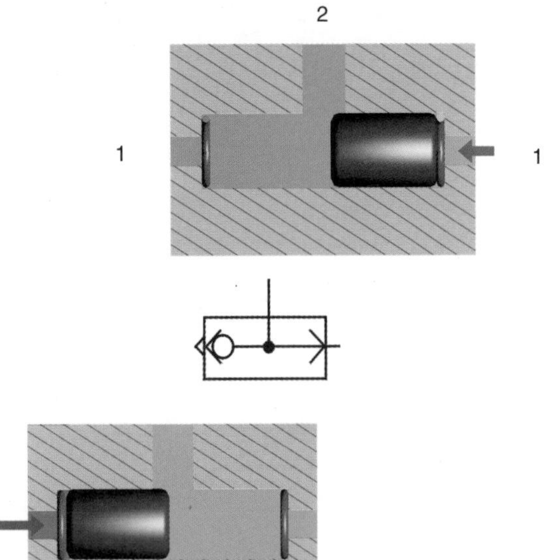

This valve has two inlets '1' and one outlet '2'.

It is useful in circuits where the start function can be operated from one of two positions on a machine or where air signals come from two separate sources to give one output.

Each of the inlets is connected to one of the start valves. If there is no input, there is no output.

However, if an air signal is received air flows to the outlet. Entry of air from one inlet blocks the other inlet via the shuttle assembly.

In other words, the shuttle valve allows air to flow through from one "OR" the other of the two inlets. For this reason, the shuttle valve is also known as an "OR" valve. An example is the pneumatic brake system of a bus which can be operated by either the foot brake "OR" the handbrake.

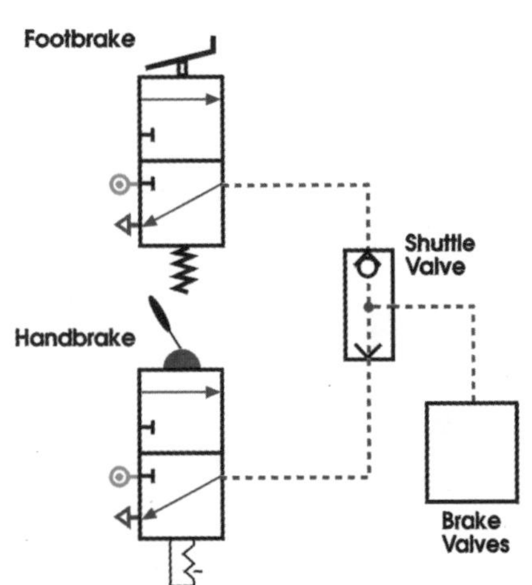

The driver's manual operation of either of these valves actuates the brakes via the shuttle valves.

The footbrake and handbrake are connected to the two inlets of the shuttle valve, whose outlet leads ultimately to the rear and front brake valves.

If both handbrake and footbrake are applied at the same time compressed air is supplied to both inlet ports simultaneously.

If one shuttle valve input receives a higher pressure this will seal the port delivering the lower pressure.

The higher inlet pressure is delivered, via the shuttle outlet, to operate the brake valves.

Quick Exhaust Valve

This valve is used to rapidly exhaust the air direct to atmosphere.

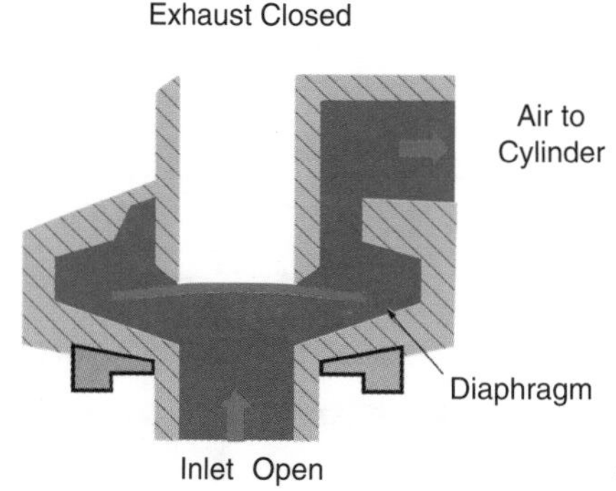

In practice the exhaust air of a cylinder has to pass through a pipe or tube which could be of considerable length. Then it goes through the directional control valve before it escapes to the atmosphere.

This pathway can act as a restriction. To avoid this restriction, a quick exhaust valve is placed at the cylinder port. This will allow the air to exhaust directly to the atmosphere.

Many industrial applications use quick exhaust valves where rapid extension or retraction of cylinders are required. One example is the impact press.

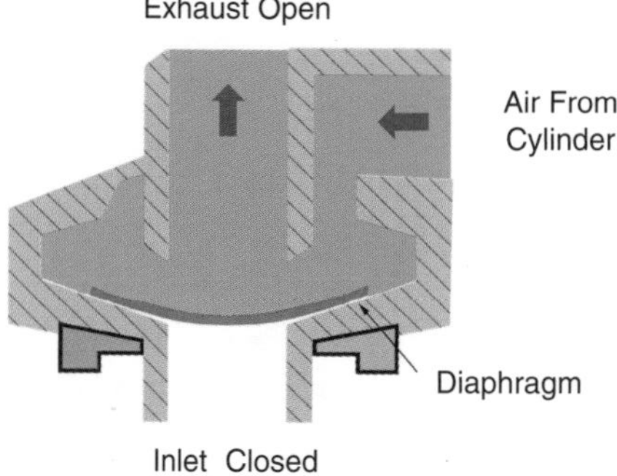

The quick exhaust valve has an inlet port, an outlet port leading to an actuator and an exhaust port open to atmosphere. The body of the valve houses a diaphragm. In some valves, there is also a spring.

When the actuator is moving air enters the inlet port and holds the diaphragm against the exhaust port seat. This allows the actuator to operate normally.

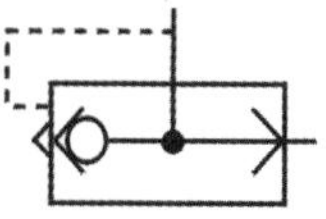

When the actuator is required to move at maximum speed the exhausting air moves the diaphragm to block the inlet port.

The air then exhausts directly, via the exhaust port, to the atmosphere.

Pneumatic Pressure Switch

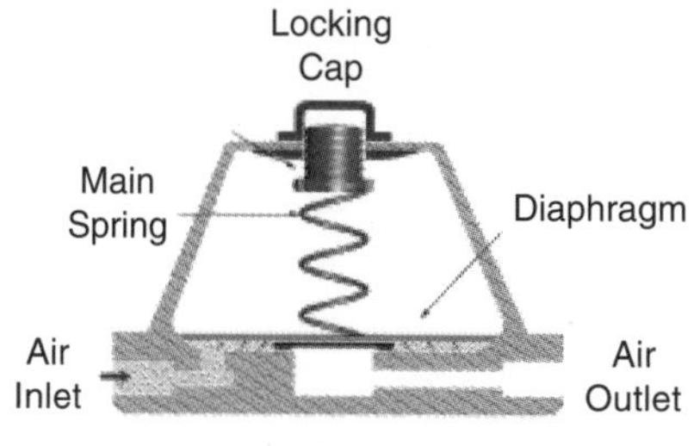

This valve produces an output at a predetermined pressure. The load on the spring is preset by the adjusting screw. This sets the pressure at which the valve will be operated.

When the air inlet pressure reaches the preset pressure on the diaphragm, enough force is developed to overcome the spring setting. The valve then opens. This valve could be used as a **Sequence** valve, ensuring that the right pressure is available in a system before a sequence of operation commences.

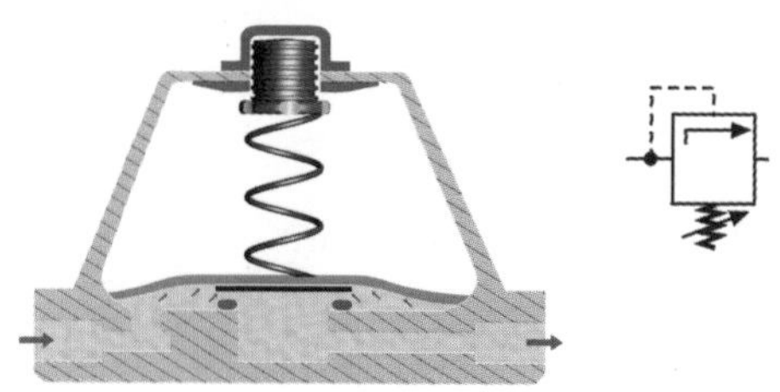

It could be used for signalling an emergency stop valve in the event of an increase in pressure above the maximum permitted.

Pneumatic / Electrical pressure switches can also give an electrical output. This can be used as a control device or give a warning of high or low pressure situations. Clockwise rotation of the adjustable screw increases the required pressure, counterclockwise decreases the required pressure.

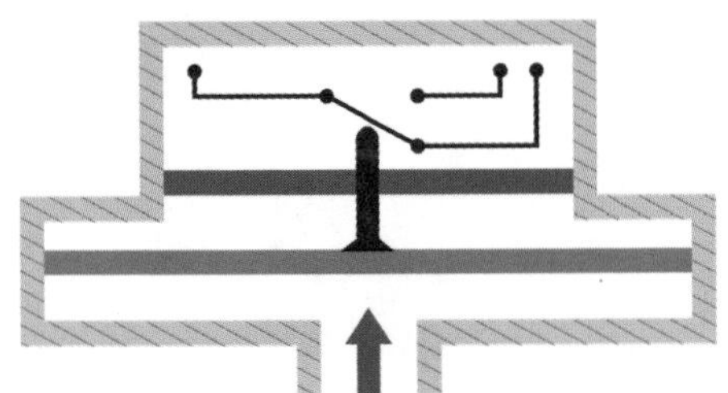

Pneumatic Timer

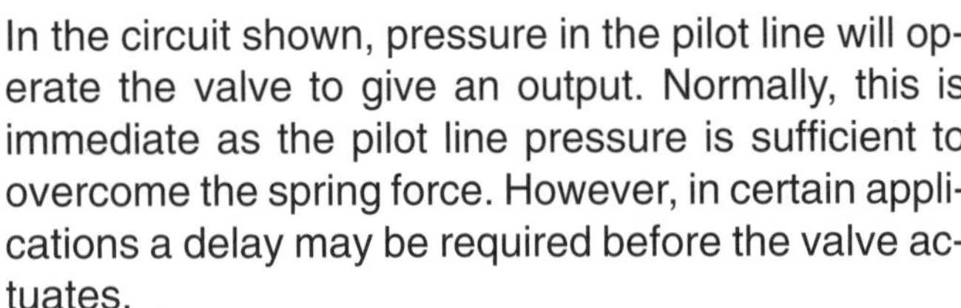

In the circuit shown, pressure in the pilot line will operate the valve to give an output. Normally, this is immediate as the pilot line pressure is sufficient to overcome the spring force. However, in certain applications a delay may be required before the valve actuates.

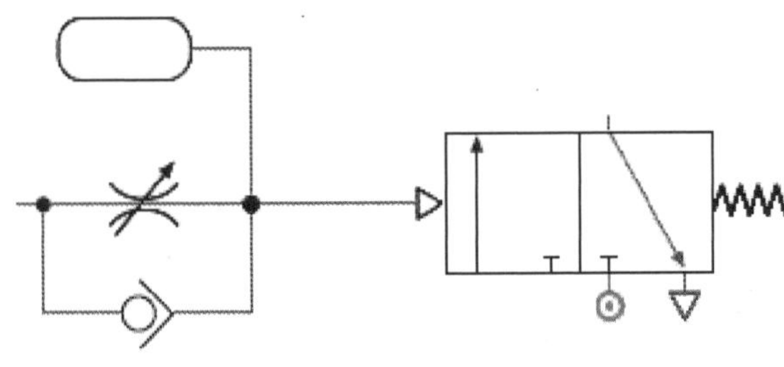

For example, it may be necessary to delay the retraction or extension of a cylinder. A pneumatic timer inserted into the pilot line allows this to be achieved.

The simplest form of a timer is to place a reservoir or volume chamber, which has a specific volume, into the pipeline. This will give a short delay in the buildup of pressure as the chamber fills up with air and is compressed.

The air supplied to a pneumatic timer must be clean and dry. Water or oil could enter the reservoir or volume chamber which would reduce its capacity (volume). This would affect the function of the timer and reduce the time delay. Longer time delays will require a larger chamber, which would be out of proportion to the rest of the circuit. Therefore, a flow control is incorporated upstream of the reservoir.

This allows the air flow to be controlled into the volume chamber further delaying the buildup in pressure. By incorporating a check valve around the flow control any delay in the resetting of the valve to its neutral position, by exhausting of pilot pressure, is removed.

This is a **timed on** circuit.

If the check valve is reversed the air signal to the output valve will bypass the flow control orifice and operate the valve immediately.

When the pilot signal is turned off, the pilot line pressure must be exhausted via the flow control. This delays the return of the output valve to its initial position. This is a **timed off** circuit.

Silencers

Silencers are made from various materials ranging from porous plastic to bronze and are screwed into exhaust ports of valves.

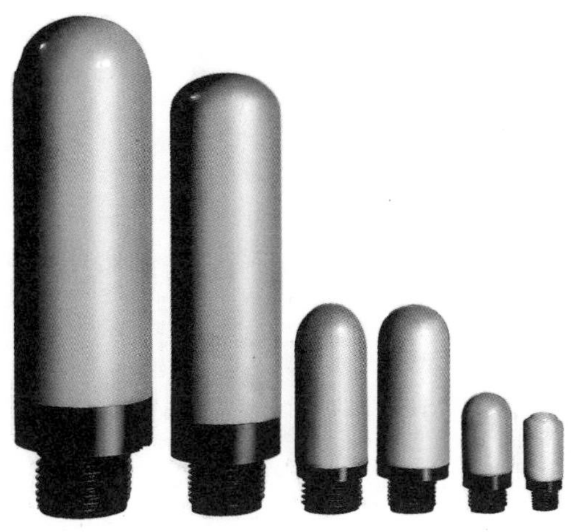

However silencers or mufflers as they are sometimes called not only reduce noise, they can also act as filters to stop contaminants entering the valve exhaust ports.

This ensures longer life and less maintenance of the system.

Silencers should be checked regularly to ensure that they are not becoming blocked and therefore setting up a back pressure in the system.

This back pressure may operate valves which could lead to a dangerous situation.

When selecting a silencer, Noise Safety Standards must be met. The higher the flow rate of air exhausting to atmosphere, the louder the noise will be.

This is measured in decibels (dB). For instance, the maximum flow for a 90dB noise reading for a 1/4" port, without a silencer, is only 7.5 l/s / 15 scfm.

However, with a silencer, keeping the dB rating to 90, the flow rate can be increased to 22.5 l/s / 45 scfm.

To control velocity of actuators in certain circuits, the silencer can be incorporated with a flow restrictor.

This is normally placed in the exhaust port.

Check the directional control valve manufacturers data to ensure that the back pressure, created by the restrictor, is acceptable.

Summary

- Valves control the direction, velocity and sequence of actuator movement.

Directional Control Valves

- Directional control valves stop, start and direct air to various parts of the circuit.
- The two main types of valve are spool and poppet.
- 2/2 valves generally act as on/off devices.
- 3/2 valves are commonly used to direct air to and from single acting cylinders. They are used as proof of position valves or limit switches.
- 4/2 valves or 5/2 valves are generally used in circuits to operate double acting cylinders. They can also be used in more complex circuits todirect air flow.
- 5/3 valves can be used in a variety of roles including acting as a safety device.

Valve Actuators

- All valves require some form of actuation to move the spool or poppet.
- The actuation may be manual, mechanical, electrical, or pneumatic.

Flow Control Valves

- Flow control valves control the velocity of actuators.
- Both variable and fixed orifice restrictors can be used to give the required flow rate.

- The check valve allows flow control in one direction and unrestricted flow in the reverse direction.

Accessory Valves And Equipment

- The Shuttle valve has two inlets and one outlet. It is useful where a start function can be operated from two positions. The shuttle valve is also known as an 'OR' valve.
- The Quick Exhaust valve is used to exhaust air quickly from an actuator port.
- The Pneumatic Pressure Switch produces a pneumatic output at a pre-determined pressure.
- The Pneumatic Timer delays a signal for a pre-determined length of time.
- Silencers can be fitted to exhaust ports of valves to reduce noise levels.
- Silencers should be maintained regularly to check for blockages which can create a backpressure.

Introduction To Pneumatic Equipment Energy Output Devices / Actuators

Objectives

In this section we will be examining:

- the parts of a pneumatic cylinder
- pneumatic cylinder cushioning
- calculations of force generated by, and pressures required for, cylinder operation
- rotary actuators
- pneumatic motor types and sizing

Linear Motion

Pneumatic Cylinders

The pneumatic cylinder or ram is probably the best known of all pneumatic actuators.

It converts pneumatic pressure and flow into force and linear motion.

Pneumatic cylinders can operate very fast. They are used in many industrial applications and can:

- push
- pull
- transfer
- stamp
- clamp
- cut

They range from 4mm (3/8 in.) bore up to 350mm (14 in.) bore and can be supplied in many different lengths.

They are capable of reacting quickly to changes in air supply direction.

Four main types of cylinders are used in pneumatic systems.

Single Acting Cylinder

This is powered in one direction only.

It returns to its original position as a result of an external force such as gravity or a load, or by an internal spring.

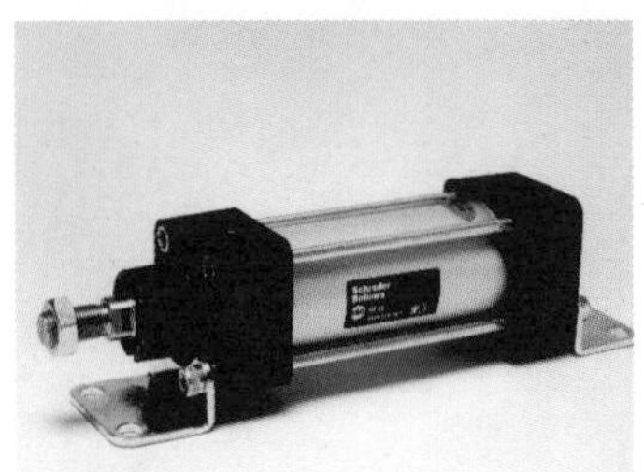

Double Acting Cylinder

This is powered by compressed air for both the extend and the retract strokes.

Diaphragm Actuator

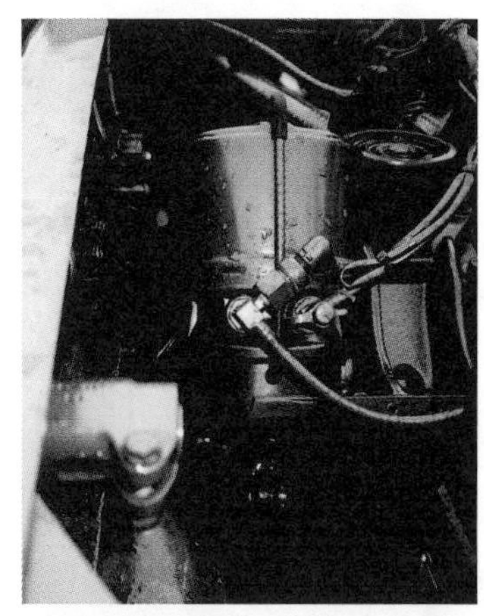

This makes it ideal for continuous operation in hostile environments, such as motor vehicles.

It has a short stroke in relation to the diaphragm size. This makes for a powerful unit.

Due to this power/weight and size relationship it is used extensively in vehicle braking systems.

Rodless Cylinders

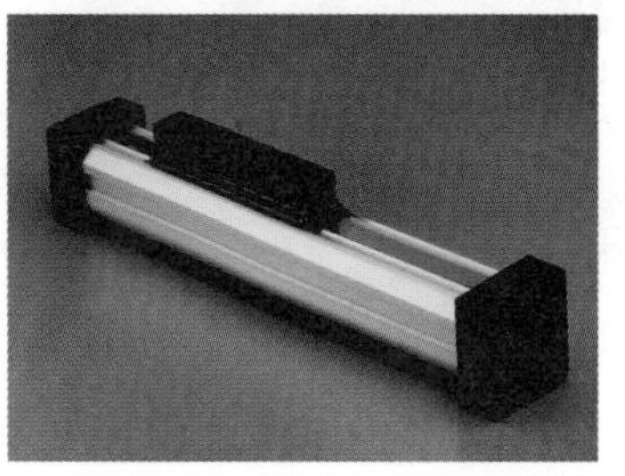

Rodless cylinders are of the double acting type and are ideal for compact installations or in applications where space is limited.

Cylinder Construction

Barrel / Piston

The barrel - or tube - of a pneumatic cylinder can be made of aluminium/aluminum, brass, steel or stainless steel. The material used depends upon the working environment. It is normally polished honed or skived internally to reduce **friction**. The thickness of the wall is determined by the pressure the cylinder has to withstand and its internal bore size.

Piston

The piston can be made of, aluminium, steel or stainless steel.

It separates the rear and front compartments of the barrel.

Piston rod

The piston rod is normally made of steel or stainless steel, depending on the application.

It is usually polished or chromed to reduce friction. The diameter is determined at the design stage, based on:

- the thrust force to be encountered
- the length of **stroke**, i.e., the distance that the piston rod travels

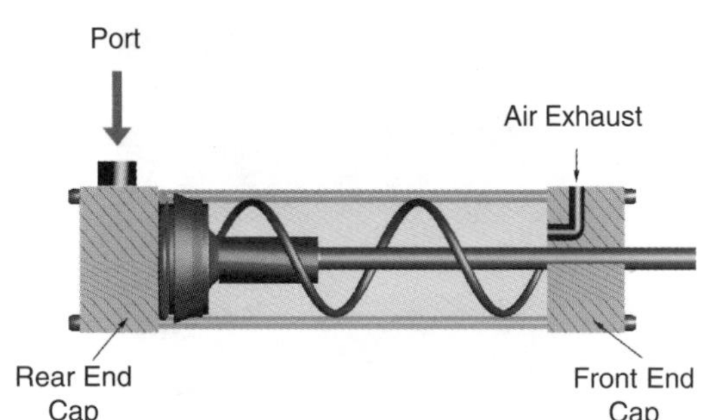

At the ends of the cylinder barrel are the **end caps**.

The cap that the piston rod passes through is called the **front end cap**, **head** or **rod-end**. The one at the back end of the cylinder barrel is called the **rear end cap** or **cap**.

In a single acting cylinder there is a threaded port on the **rear end cap** or cap, which allows the compressed air to enter and leave.

To ensure cylinder movement the front end cap or head allows the air to exit through a small vent hole.

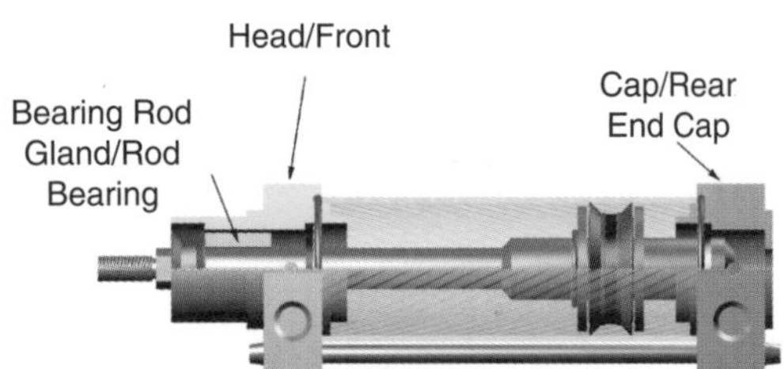

In a double acting cylinder, both the head and cap have threaded ports to allow entry and exit of air.

The **front end** or **head** contains a **bearing rod**, **gland** or **rod bearing** that helps to minimize any lateral movement of the piston rod.

Various methods are used to secure the end caps to the cylinder barrel. They can be:

- screwed / threaded
- bolted
- crimped
- secured with tie bars / rods
- lock rings

Seals

Seals are used to prevent leakage while avoiding any significant increase in friction.

Seals are found:

- On the **piston**

- Between the piston and **piston rod**.

This prevents air leaking through the center of the piston

- Between the **caps** and the barrel.

This seal prevents air leaking past the caps and the barrel to the atmosphere

- On the front end cap or head

This seal prevents air leaking past the piston rod atmosphere.

The head also has a **wiper seal** to prevent contaminants entering the cylinder.

This is generally of a soft seal material.

This is also known as a **scraper** seal if the material is harder such as metal.

If the cylinder is of the cushion type, the caps contain the seal for this purpose.

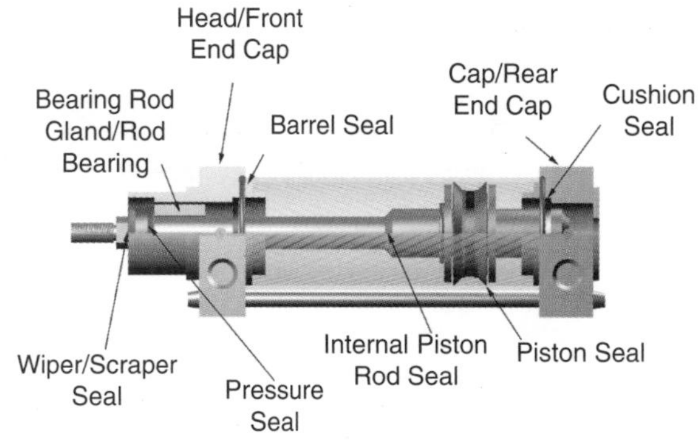

Cushioning

Pneumatic cylinders can operate at very high velocities. At such velocities, there can be a powerful impact between the piston and the end caps.

This could result in damage to the cylinder or connected machinery. A form of end cushioning is used to avoid this problem.

When the piston begins to move toward the end cap it pushes air out of the end cap port. The rapid exit of the air allows the piston to move at maximum velocity.

A boss or sleeve is placed on the piston. When this enters the flow passage of the end cap, the main airway is cut off. Now air can only be metered through an adjustable orifice.

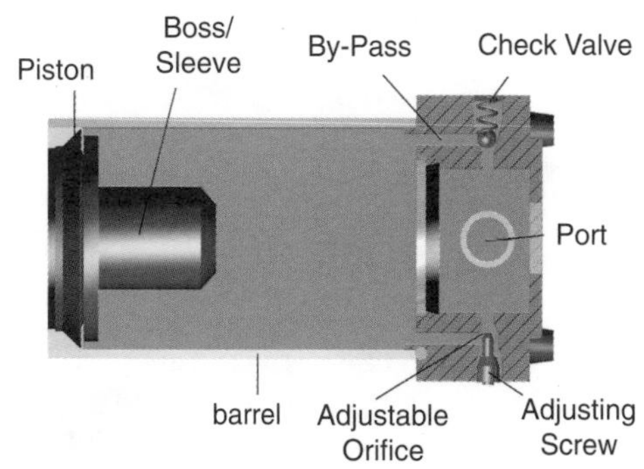

As the air can only leave through this narrower port, the piston is slowed by a resulting increase in pressure.

This slowing of the piston 'cushions' the impact between the piston and the end cap.

However, when the piston moves in the opposite direction, the boss would inhibit its starting force.

So a bypass element is incorporated into the cushioning device. This consists of a ball check valve.

This check valve ensures that air is only allowed through the adjusting screw when the piston boss enters the cap.

When the piston has to move in the opposite direction the air pressure opens the check valve.

The air can now act on the large piston area, giving maximum starting force. This means a cushioned cylinder can start quickly.

Some cylinders have adjustable cushioning at both ends of the cylinder. This allows the engineer to set the most efficient slow down rate.

Fig. 1

Fig. 2

Fig. 3

Fig. 4

Mountings

All cylinders need to be mounted securely to ensure maximum efficiency, ease of movement and safe machine operation.

The cylinder itself can have various mountings including leg brackets, trunnions and nose (head) mountings.

Piston rods can be screwed directly into mechanisms or use a piston rod clevis.

Fig 1. Shows an actuator mounted by a rear **trunnion.**

Fig 2. Shows an actuator with a **rear eye** mounting.

Fig 3. Shows an actuator with a **hinge bracket.**

Fig 4. The piston rod mounting here is a **clevis.** Where a small amount of angular movement is required a spherical rod end is attached to the piston rod.

Rodless Cylinders

Rodless cylinders are of the double acting type and are ideal for compact installations or in applications where space is limited.

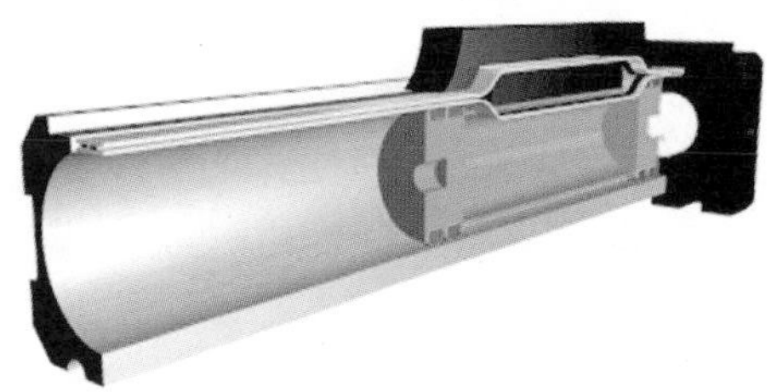

The installation length of a Rodless cylinder is only slightly longer than the cylinders stroke.

Rodless cylinders can be used in 50% less space than conventional double acting cylinders.

The carriage is attached to the piston and is separated by a stainless steel band.

As the carriage moves along the upper seal cleans and resets the band.

This keeps contaminants from entering the sealing area of the cylinder.

Air Bellows

Air bellows are used where applications require short stroke, high thrust, single acting actuators.

Air bellows are manufactured from reinforced synthetic rubber.

No reciprocating metal parts are incorporated into the construction, which provides virtually frictionless thrust.

Single, double and triple convolution versions give variable stroke combinations.

The return stroke of these units are provided by the natural spring action of the bellows and the load itself.

Little maintenance is required, even under arduous conditions.

The mounting of air bellows is less critical than conventional rigid pneumatic cylinders due to their flexible construction.

Angular misalignment of up to 15 degrees maximum is acceptable along with axial misalignment of up to 10mm (3/8in).

Air bellows are very versatile, however, external mechanical stops should be used so that maximum 'stroke length' and 'bottoming out' do not occur.

Calculations

Force Requirements

For a cylinder to move, two factors must be overcome:

- The resistance of the piston to movement, primarily, due to friction.
- The weight of the load to be moved

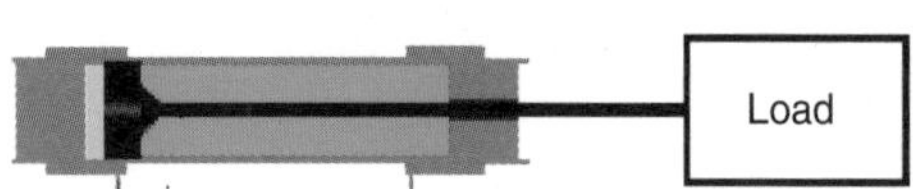

It is important to remember that in pistons with a single rod, the areas on opposite faces of the piston will differ. While air pressure can work on the full face of one side of the piston, it can only act on the full area **minus** the area covered by the piston rod, on the other face. The remaining area is known as the "Effective Area".

So, the force generated by a fixed pressure, on the **extend** phase of an actuator, will be greater than the force generated on the **retraction** or return phase of the actuator movement due to a smaller surface area. These cylinders are therefore known as **differential type cylinders.**

For double rod cylinders, the area for compressed air to work is the same. This results in equal forces being produced on both movements of the cylinder. These are known as **non-differential** type cylinders.

Velocity / Speed

There are many variables that determine the velocity of a pneumatic cylinder. The main ones are:

- Working area
- Stroke
- Valve size

- Pipe bore size
- Flow rate
- Exhaust capacity (Flow Rate)

Most manufacturers of pneumatic equipment provide data sheets of the maximum flow rates for their valves.

Pneumatic directional control valves are customarily rated industrially by a flow coefficient known as its `$C_v$` rating.

The larger the C_v the more air flow the valve can handle.

If velocity is critical then consult the manufacturer.

Rotary Actuators / Motors

Rotary actuators and air motors are particularly useful in areas that could be inflammable, explosive or wet.

Positive air pressure keeps dust and moisture out of the mechanism. The air also ensures that they will not overheat when running at high speed.

An advantage of air motors over electric motors is that they can be stalled with full air pressure without fear of damage occurring.

Semi-rotary motion or limited rotation is achieved by using a pneumatic cylinder connected to a Rack and Pinion mechanism.

The cylinder rod is connected to a gear rack, which in turn rotates the pinion.

Linear motion is therefore converted to rotary motion.

Rotary motion can also be achieved by incorporating a semi-rotary vane within a cylinder body.

Both the rack and pinion and vane type units are called rotary actuators.

Motor Types

Air motors have many uses, including construction tools, hoists, conveyors and portable hand tools.

There are three main types of motors:

- The vane.
- The piston.
- The turbine.

Air is delivered under pressure to the operating mechanism which gives rotary motion.

Unidirectional motors rotate in one direction only.

Bi-directional motors rotate both clockwise and counterclockwise.

Motor Selection

The rotary force given by a motor is called **torque.**

Torque is the force that is present at a distance from the center of a motor shaft.

The unit for measuring torque is the Newton-metre or pound-inch.

In this example, a force of 250N is applied at a distance of 0.5m from the center of a motor shaft.

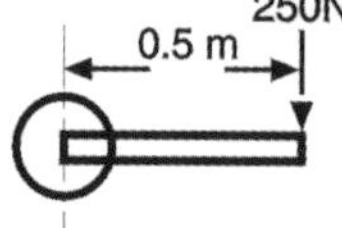

To calculate the torque, the force is multiplied by the distance.

The resultant torque is 125Nm.

Using US units, a force of 50lbf is positioned on a bar which is attached to a motor shaft at a distance of 10in.

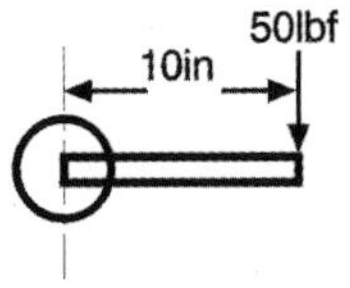

50lbf
10in

To calculate the torque (turning effort) at the shaft, the force is multiplied by the distance.

The resultant torque is 500 lb-in.

Motor Velocity

Just as with pneumatic cylinders, a number of factors determine motor velocity.

The main ones are:

- Working area
- Valve size
- Pipe bore size
- Flow rate
- Exhaust capacity

Most manufacturers provide an indication of motor velocity in revolutions per minute, for a certain air flow and pressure, together with all the relevant data which affects it.

As with all system actuator requirements, if in doubt, always consult the manufacturer.

Summary

Pneumatic Cylinders

Pneumatic cylinders convert compressed air pressure into linear force and motion.

There are two main types of cylinder; single acting and double acting.

Their barrels or bodies can be made of aluminum, brass, steel or stainless steel. A piston, separates the cap and head (rod end) of the cylinder.

The piston rod is generally polished steel or stainless steel. Seals are placed on the piston, the head and between the piston and piston rod to prevent air moving from one side of the cylinder to another.

The caps can incorporate a cushioning device to prevent powerful impacts between the piston and the caps.

Air enters and exits the cylinder through the caps that are connected to the barrel in a variety of ways.

Cylinders can be mounted in a variety of ways, depending upon the application.

Pascal's Law can be used to calculate the required pressure, for a given cylinder, to apply the desired force.

Rotary Motion

Semi-rotary motion or limited rotation can be achieved by a rack and pinion.

A further method or achieving semi-rotary motion is the vane cylinder.

This is suitable for applications such as opening and closing valves.

Rotary motion can be achieved in a variety of ways.

The main types of motor are the vane, piston and turbine.

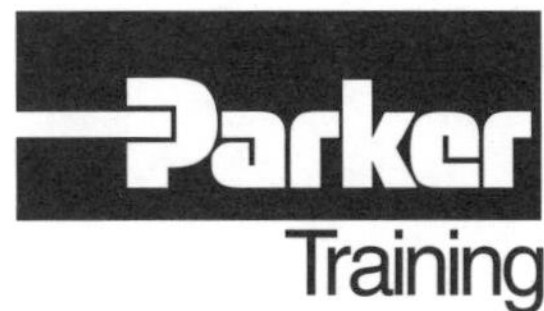

Module 4

Circuit Design/Basic Circuits

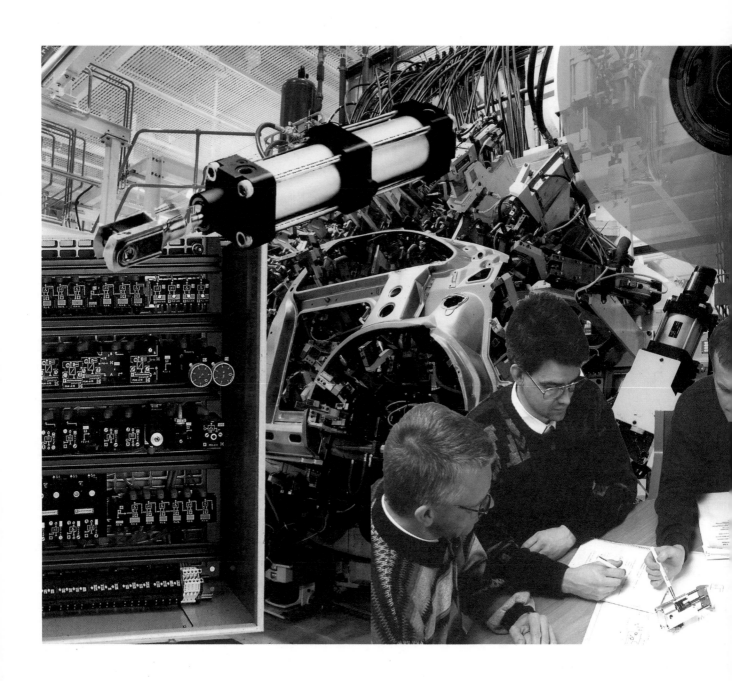

Contents

Circuit Design / Basic Circuits

Objectives

In this section the following will be examined:

- The conventions for circuit diagram layout.
- The basic circuits and flow control involving single acting cylinders.
- The basic circuits and flow control of circuits involving double acting cylinders.
- Remote control and automatic control of double acting cylinder circuits.
- Time delay and sequential control of double acting cylinder circuits.
- Different types of circuits including two hand starts, guard circuits, slow pressure initialization and fail safe circuits.

Design Principles

Circuit Diagrams

Circuit diagrams are a crucial part of pneumatic technology, just as they are for hydraulic, electric or electronic systems. They allow the:

- Engineer to pipe a circuit correctly
- Maintenance engineer to find faults quickly and safely
- Designer to modify a circuit

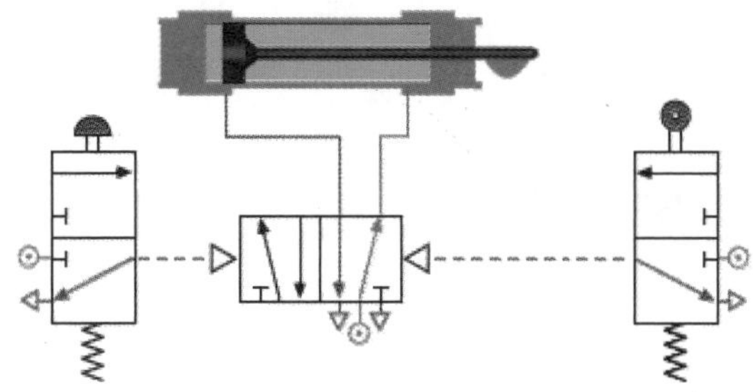

A circuit diagram also informs personnel of any equipment that may need special attention.

Circuit diagrams assist in devising maintenance schemes that can minimize any breakdowns in the system.

Throughout this section the symbols used are to the ISO 1219 standard.

Circuit Layout

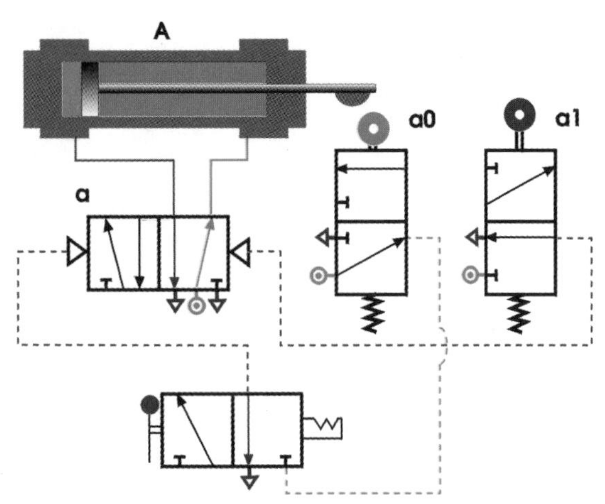

Circuits should be laid out in accordance with standards laid down by ISO or to good custom and practice.

The circuit shown here is one method used which has the limit / proof of position valves at the cylinder end positions.

On larger circuits this produces "spaghetti junctions" (lines crossing) which can be confusing.

The circuit shown here is the same as the previous circuit but has been redrawn to be read more easily.

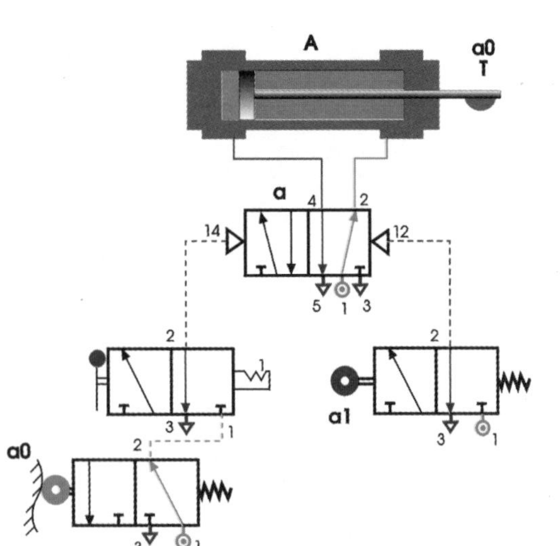

Cylinders are shown at the top of the page facing left to right.

Directional control valves are placed below the cylinder.

Switches or signal generators (devices) are placed below and to the side of the directional control valves.

Limit valves, or **proof of position** valves, are not shown in their corresponding cylinder position.

Their normal positions are marked with a 'T' symbol and given a reference, in this case 'a0' and 'a1'.

They are shown in the circuit operating the directional control valve.

Cylinder and Valve Identification

Valves and actuators in circuit diagrams are identified so that anyone looking at the diagram can see which valve operates which cylinder. This is especially useful in multi-actuator circuits.

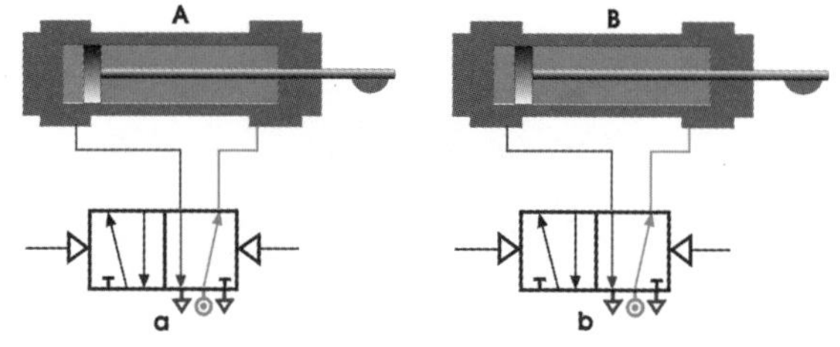

Cylinder	Valve
A	a
B	b
C	c

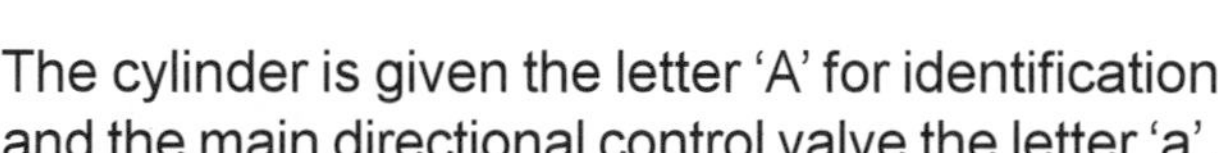

The cylinder is given the letter 'A' for identification and the main directional control valve the letter 'a'.

The left hand pilot when operated will change valve 'a' and cylinder 'A' will extend.

When the left hand pilot is reset and the right hand pilot operated, the directional control valve 'a' will return to its original position and cylinder 'A' will retract.

Numbering System

A further version which is used throughout Europe uses a numbering system to identify cylinders and valves.

Thus, cylinders are numbered, from left to right, as 1.0, 2.0, 3.0 etc. The corresponding directional control valves are numbered as:

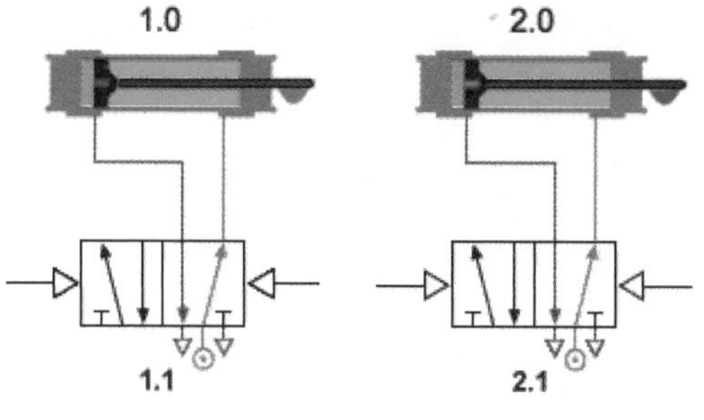

Cylinder	Valve
1.0	1.1
2.0	2.1
3.0	3.1
etc.	etc.

Limit or signal valves (devices) which operate a directional control valve are numbered according to whether they cause the control valve to **extend** or **retract** the cylinder.

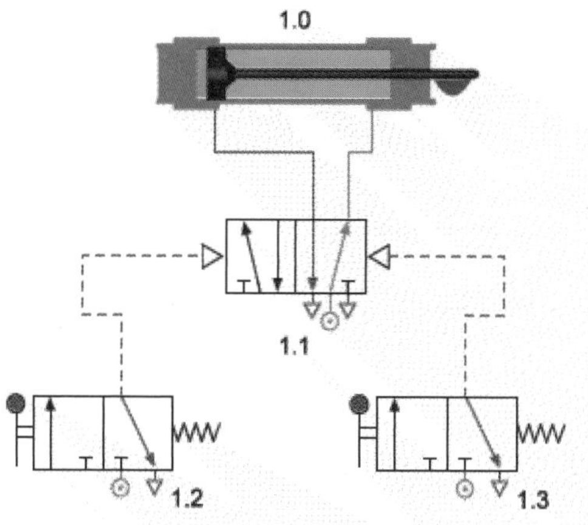

Limit or signal valves (devices) operating directional control valves that **extend** the cylinder are **even** numbers to that cylinder's relevant number. Thus, to extend cylinder 1.0, directional control valve 1.1 is operated by signal valve (device) 1.2.

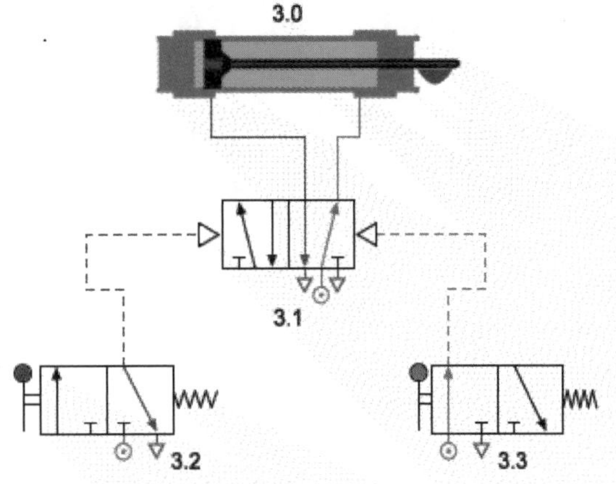

So, a signal valve (device) with the designation 1.3 will operate directional control valve 1.1 to **retract** cylinder 1.0.

Shown here is part of a larger circuit where there are at least three cylinders. Note that the reference number given to the cylinder is 3.0, the reference for the direction control valve is therefore 3.1.

The lever / spring 3/2 valve, when operated, will **extend** cylinder 3.0 and is therefore given the reference 3.2.

The lever / spring 3/2 valve which **retracts** cylinder 3.0 is given the reference 3.3

Cylinder and valve references are generally only used in multi-actuator circuits for ease of identification.

Basic Circuits

Single Acting Cylinder Circuits

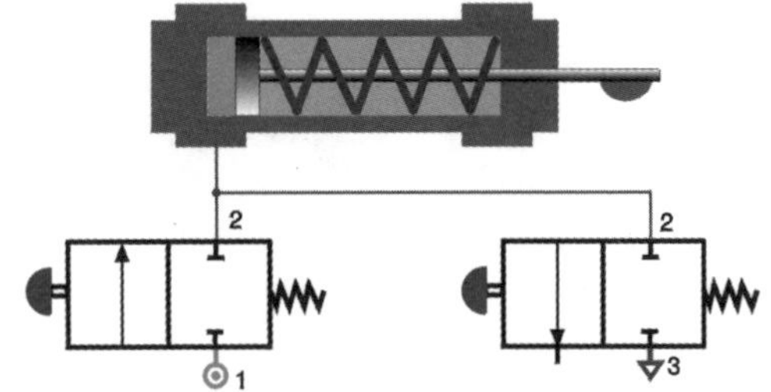

A single acting cylinder can be operated by a pair of 2/2 directional control valves, both normally closed (non passing).

By operating the left hand power valve, the cylinder will extend.

By operating the right hand power valve, the cylinder will retract.

Both valves must **not** be operated simultaneously as the air from the left hand power valve will exhaust through the right hand power valve.

2/2 valves are rarely used as directional control valves in circuits as they do not have an exhaust port, but this shows what can be achieved with simple 2/2 valves.

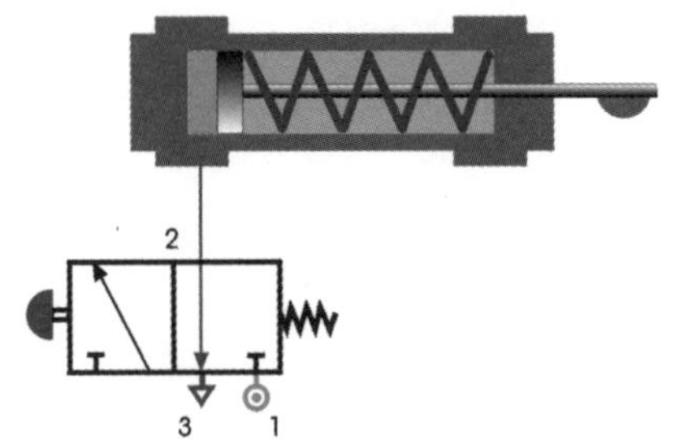

3/2 valves therefore are commonly used. This **normally closed / non passing** valve keeps the cylinder retracted.

By pushing the button, the cylinder is extended. On release of the push button the spring returns the valve to its "Neutral" / Initial or "at rest" position. Air is exhausted and the cylinder retracts.

Port numbering has also been added to the 3/2 valve.

An alternative arrangement is to use a normally open / passing valve. Here, air is supplied to the cylinder when the valve is in its at rest position. Thus the cylinder is extended. When the valve is operated, the cylinder retracts.

Flow Control

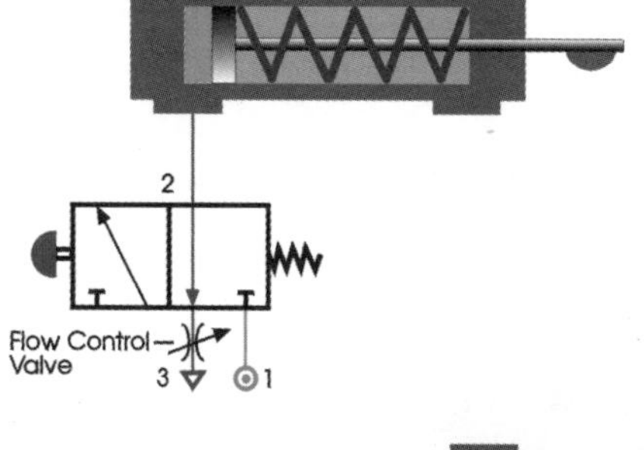

Cylinder velocity may have to be adjusted or controlled in certain applications.

Here, an adjustable flow control valve is placed in the 3/2 valve exhaust port and adjusted to allow the cylinder to **retract** slowly.

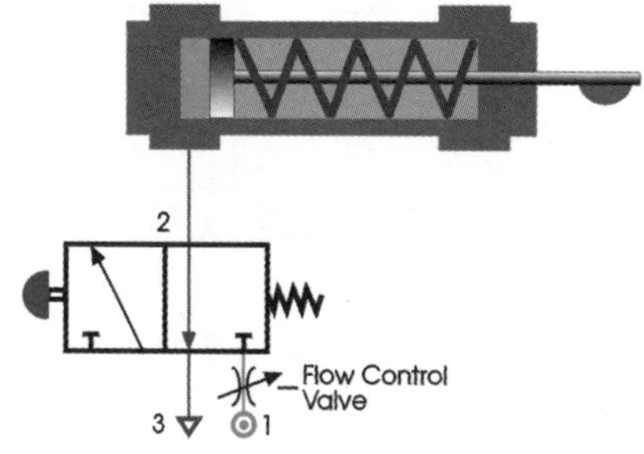

Note: Not all valve designs permit operation with a restricted exhaust port. Check manufacturer's data.

Switching the position of the flow control valve to the supply line of the 3/2 valve allows slow **extension** of the cylinder.

Double Acting Cylinder Circuits

Double acting cylinders are powered both on the extension stroke and retraction stroke and therefore require valves with two working / cylinder ports, which can be connected to the ports of the cylinder.

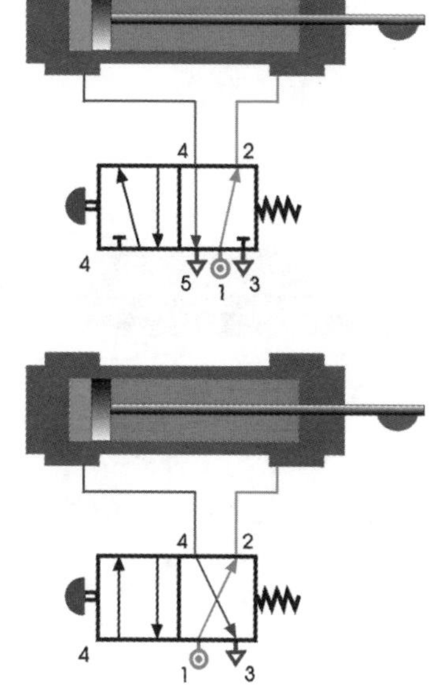

Both 5/2 and 4/2 valves can perform this task. In both cases, when the valve is activated, the cylinder extends.

The 5/2 valve has an extra exhaust port '5'.

With both these types of valves, whenever the button is released, the valve spring automatically returns the valve to the initial or at rest position.

The cylinder will therefore retract under air power.

Before the air is turned on to any cylinder circuit, the port connections should be checked. If con-

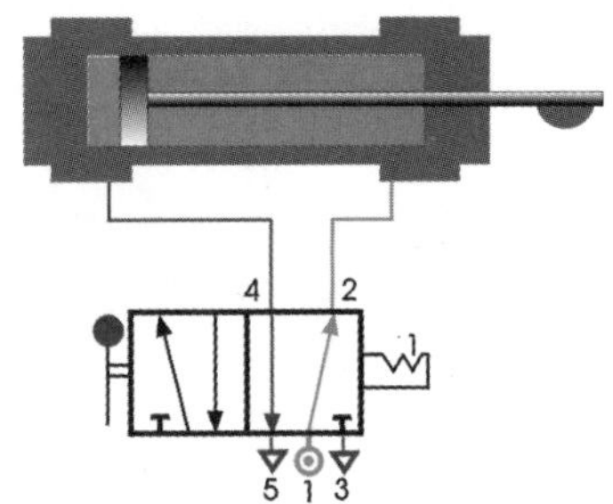

nected incorrectly, the cylinder could extend and cause injury or damage.

To prevent automatic retraction of a cylinder, a different type of actuator must be used on the valve. This is a lever / detent valve. Once the lever has been operated, the open / passing position is held by the detent. Therefore the cylinder can be left extended for any period of time.

In order to retract the cylinder, the lever must be operated again.

Flow Control

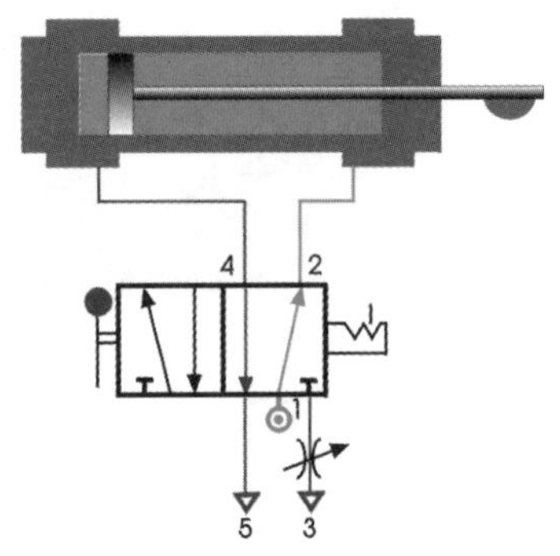

In some applications, the cylinder velocity may have to be reduced on:

- The extension stroke
- The retracting stroke
- Both the extension and retraction strokes

Here, an adjustable flow control has been placed in exhaust port '3' of the 5/2 valve.

This enables the velocity of cylinder extension to be adjusted.

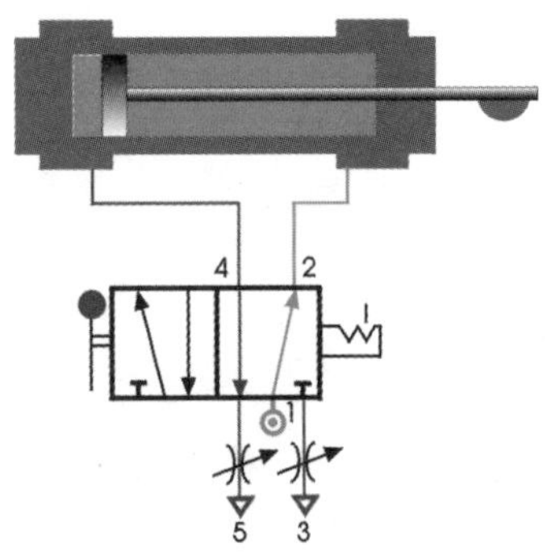

If control is required for both extension **and** retraction:

Adjustable flow control valves are placed on both exhaust ports of the valve, i.e., ports '3' and '5'.

However, the best control is achieved by placing the flow control valves at the cylinder ports or as near to them as possible.

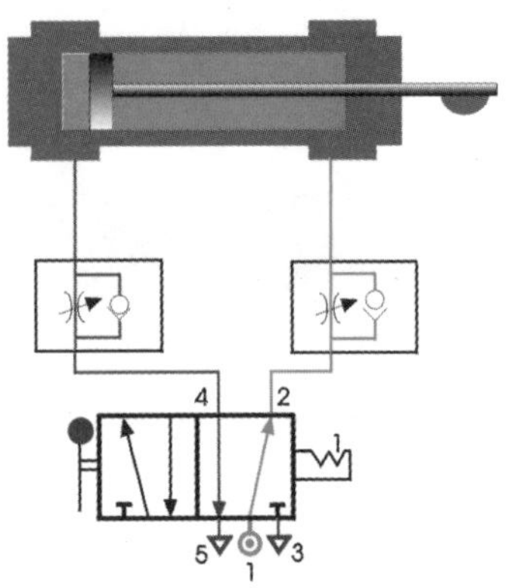

In certain countries, plant safety codes mandate this placement. This example shows two flow control valves, on the rear cap and on front or rod end ports of the cylinder.

Generally, it is the exhaust air from the cylinder that is restricted, while the air supplied to the cylinder is unrestricted.

Therefore, bypass check valves are incorporated to ensure that the air supply to the cylinder is unrestricted.

The settings on these flow control valves can be adjusted to give different velocities for extension and retraction of the cylinder.

Quick Exhaust Valves

Some applications require the cylinder to extend at a fast rate. However, this velocity can often be limited by how quickly air can be exhausted from the cylinder. This is normally via a pipe to the directional control valve and exhaust port.

However, there will be resistance to flow in this line, as well as resistance to flow through the valve. If this resistance was eliminated, the cylinder would travel faster.

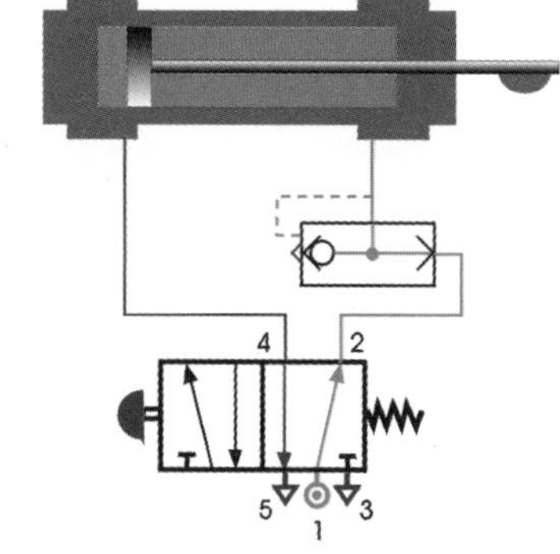

To eliminate this resistance, a quick exhaust valve is placed at or near the exhaust port of the cylinder.

When the cylinder extends, air from the cylinder operates the diaphragm inside the quick exhaust valve which isolates the exhaust from going through the system.

The air is then exhausted directly to atmosphere.

Fast Approach / Slow Feed

In some circuits it is desirable that the extension velocity phase varies. For example, some circuits require the actuator to extend rapidly at the start of extension and more slowly at the end of extension.

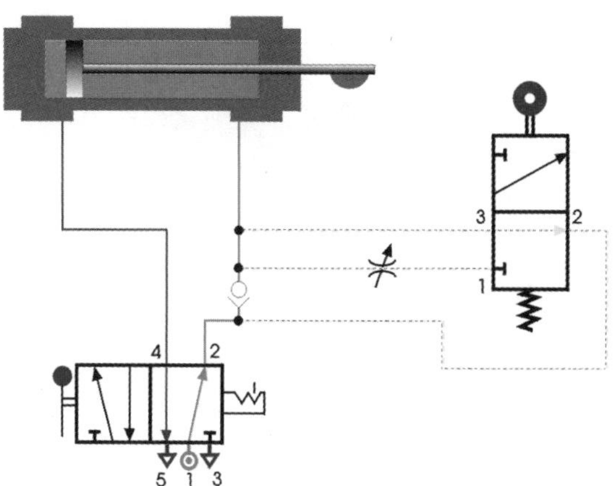

To achieve this, the following must be added to the circuit:

- A non return / check valve
- A variable restrictor (flow control) set to give a low flow rate
- A 3/2 cam roller/spring valve, of the spool type

Note: The cam roller valve is acting as a selector valve with ports '1' and '3' connected to port '2' to give the desired operation. This valve must be of the balanced spool type.

The 3/2 valve is positioned in such a way that a cam on the cylinder piston rod operates the roller actuator.

The check valve directs the air flow through the 3/2 valve during the extension stroke. During the initial extension, air flows unrestricted through the 3/2 valve to exhaust:

- Fast approach

When the cam reaches the roller on the 3/2 valve, the "fast" circuit is closed off (blocked) and the slow circuit, incorporating the needle/flow control valve, is opened.

- Slow feed

The check valve allows air to flow unrestricted to retract the cylinder.

The fast approach / slow feed / fast return circuit can also be achieved by placing a cam roller operated flow control valve in place of the 3/2 cam roller valve.

Remote Circuits

Cylinders can be operated remotely (from a distance), by incorporating signal valves (devices) into the circuit.

A pilot line has now been added to the main directional control valve. This is signaled by air supplied via a 3/2 valve, acting as a remote signal valve (device).

This signal valve (device) can be located at some distance away. It can be small in comparison to the directional control valve, as it only needs to supply a small flow of air to the valve actuator.

By pushing in the button on the signal valve (device), air flows to the pilot valve, which is activated.

Air then flows into the cylinder. To ensure full cylinder extension, the signal valve must be actuated all the time. The moment this is released, the cylinder will retract.

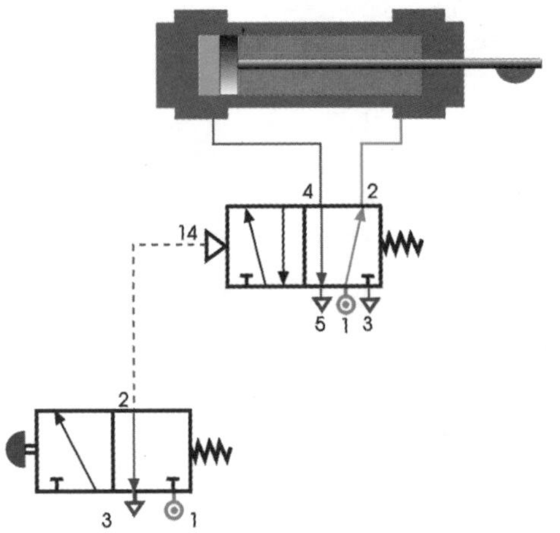

This remote control can be extended to allow extension of the cylinder from more than one point on the machine.

Here, a second power valve has been added. However, this circuit would not operate correctly.

As the circuit stands, whenever the left hand power valve was activated, the air would pass directly to the exhaust line of the right hand power valve and vice versa.

Therefore a **shuttle** valve must be included. This valve is also known as an "OR" valve and allows air to pass through, while at the same time blocking the opposite port.

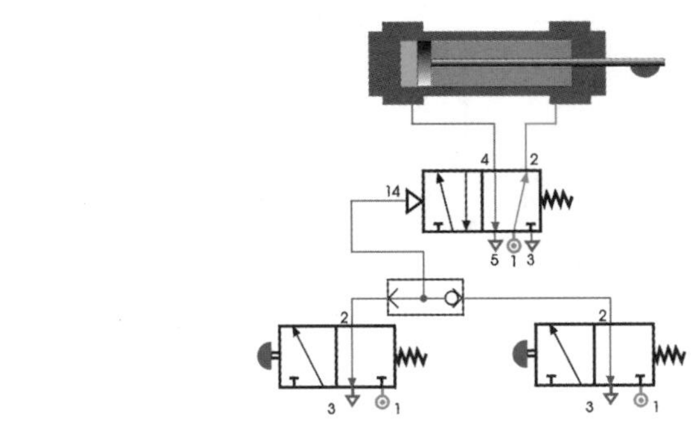

When the left hand power valve is activated, the shuttle valve blocks the flow path to the right hand power valve, and the directional control valve is operated extending the cylinder and vice versa.

Automatic Circuits

Semi-automatic Circuit

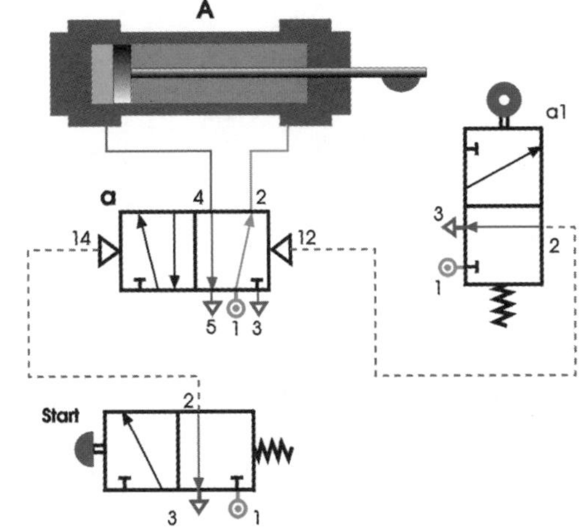

A semi-automatic circuit is one where the initiation of cylinder movement is manual, while return of the cylinder to its original position is automatic.

To achieve this, a 3/2 valve 'a1' with a cam roller actuator is placed at the full extension stroke of the cylinder.

This valve is classed as a **signal** or **proof of position** valve. It can also be called a limit switch.

Cylinder extension begins when the 'start' valve is operated.

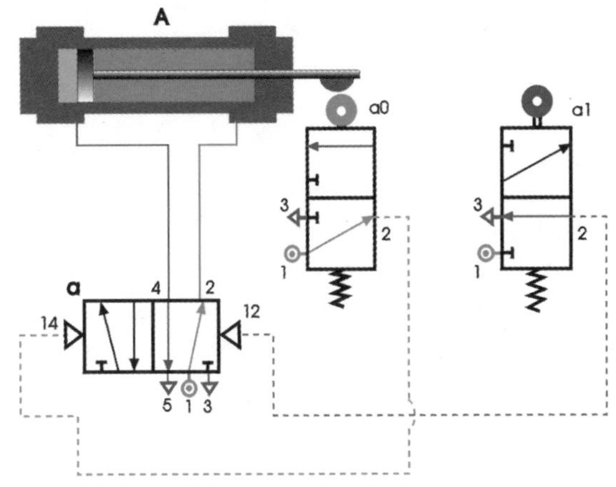

As the cylinder 'A' reaches full extension, the cam on the piston rod operates the cam roller valve 'a1'. This switches the directional control valve 'a', automatically retracting the cylinder.

Note: If the signal to port '14' is maintained (from 'start' valve), the signal from the cam roller valve 'a1' to port '12' will not operate valve 'a'. The cylinder will remain extended.

The proof of position valve 'a1' can also be used to shorten cylinder stroke length by moving it to the desired retraction position.

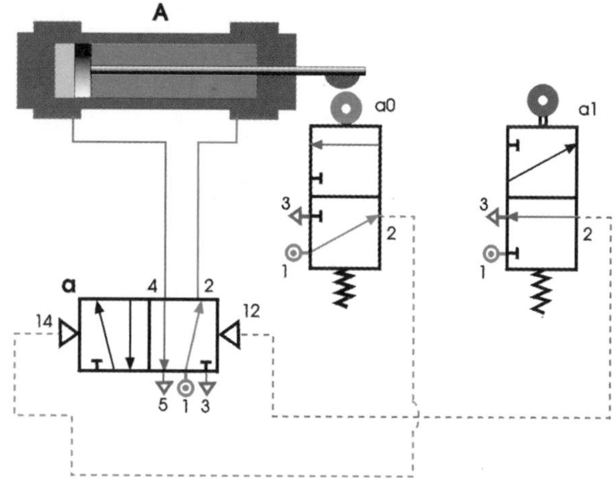

Fully Automatic Circuit

Fully automatic cycles are produced by using two normally closed / non passing 3/2 cam roller / spring valves.

Valve 'a1' is placed at the full extension stroke of the cylinder.

The second valve, 'a0', is placed in a position corresponding to the fully retracted cylinder 'A'.

When the cylinder 'A' is fully retracted, the cam on the piston rod activates the cam roller on signal limit valve 'a0'.

This, in turn, operates the directional control valve 'a', extending the cylinder.

As the cylinder extends, valve 'a0' is released and exhausts the original signal to port '14' of valve 'a'.

When cylinder 'A' is fully extended, it activates valve 'a1', switching valve 'a', retracting the cylinder, activating valve 'a0'.

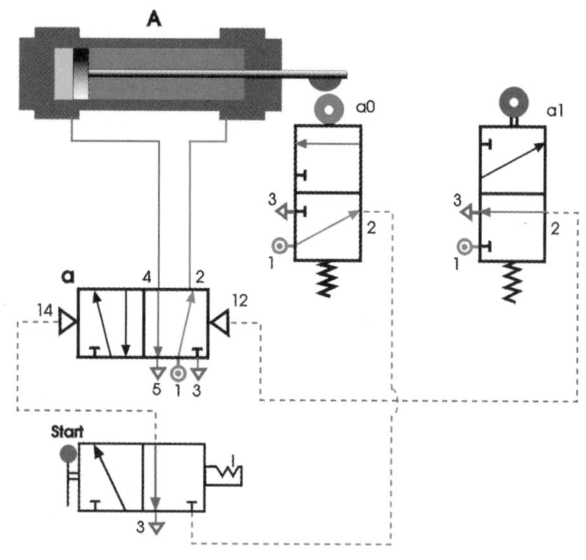

The cycle repeats continuously.

One problem with such a system is that the only way to end the cycle is to turn off the air.

However, this could result in the cylinder stopping in any position and could be dangerous.

Adding a start signal valve to the previous circuit gives a start / **stop** feature. This valve is a 3/2 normally closed / non passing lever / detent valve which is connected between valves 'a0' and 'a'.

When the **start** valve is operated, the cylinder will cycle as described earlier.

When the **start** valve is reset, the cylinder will come to rest in the retracted position, due to the signal from the cam roller valve being blocked.

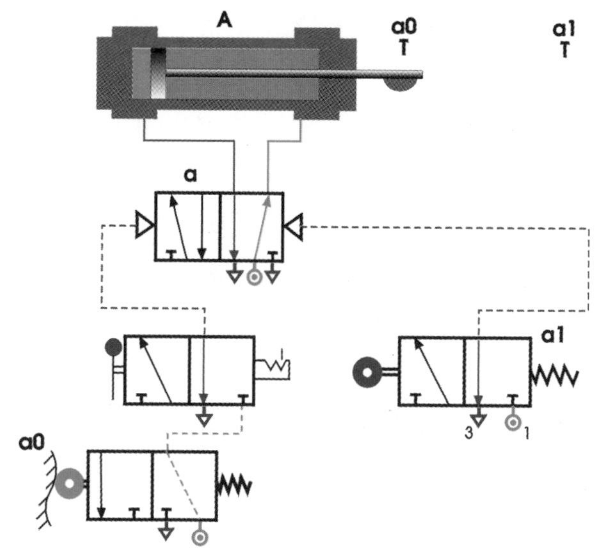

Opposite is shown the previous circuit, laid out for ease of identification and to eliminate "spaghetti junctions".

This type of control, using two valves to start a sequence, is called **series** operation.

Both the start valve **and** the proof of position valve 'a0' must be operated before the sequence starts. This type of control is also known as an 'AND' function.

Time Delay Circuits

In some applications, a time delay between the activation of the signal valve and the movement of a cylinder is required.

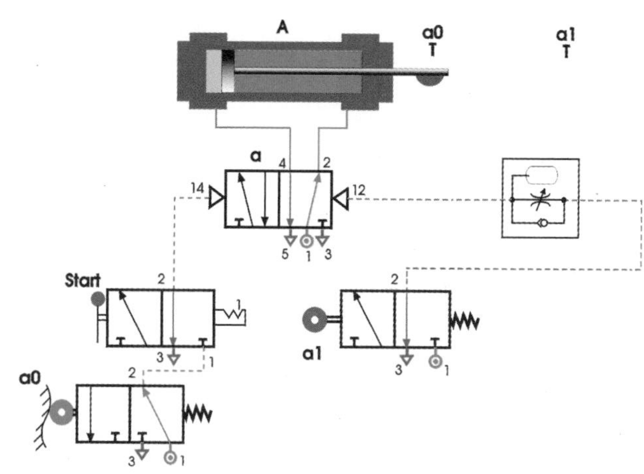

In this circuit, a time delay is required between the extension and retraction of the cylinder.

To achieve this, a **time delay valve** is incorporated into the circuit.

This consists of:

- a variable restrictor / Flow control valve
- a bypass check valve
- a reservoir

This valve is placed between signal valve 'a1' and the 5/2 directional control valve 'a'.

When the start valve is operated, the 5/2 directional control valve 'a' operates and the cylinder immediately extends.

When signal valve 'a1' is operated by the cylinder piston reaching full extension, air passes to the timer.

This 'bleeds' through the restrictor (flow control) into the reservoir (volume chamber). The bypass valve is closed (blocked). The transfer of air to the reservoir means that insufficient pressure passes to the 5/2 valve to operate it.

When the reservoir (volume chamber) is full, it allows pressure to build up, giving the desired time delay. The length of the time delay is dependent upon:

- the size of the reservoir (volume chamber)
- the setting on the variable restrictor (flow control)

When valve 'a1' is released, the air exhausts immediately via the non return / bypass valve.

When timers are used in a circuit, this part must have dry, unlubricated air.

If water or oil enters the reservoir (volume changer), it will reduce the volume and hence reduce the time delay.

Pressure Dependent Sequential Circuits

Often, cylinders within a circuit must operate in a particular sequence where pressure must be maintained before the next sequence begins.

Pressure sequence valves can be used in these circumstances.

These normally closed / non passing valves will open only when the inlet pressure exceeds a preset level.

The **stamp** cylinder should only begin to extend once the **clamp** cylinder has completed its extension and is under pressure.

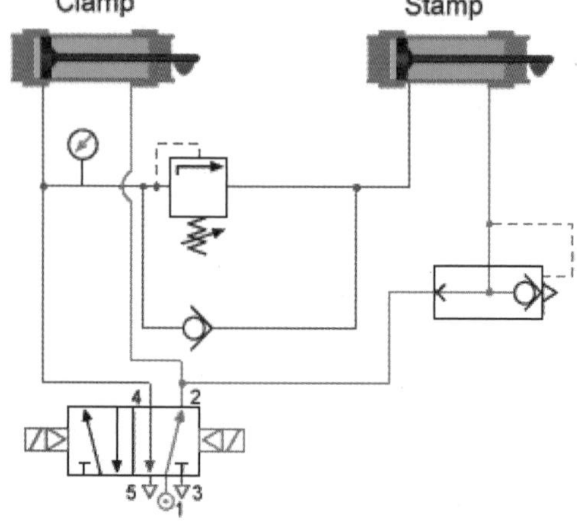

The sequence valve is placed in the circuit, isolating the stamp cylinder from the controlling 5/2 valve.

When the valve is opened, the **clamp** cylinder extends.

Initially, the pressure in the system to extend the clamp cylinder is lower than the maximum system pressure. Therefore the sequence valve remains closed.

While this circuit operates well, it does not allow for a malfunction in the sequence.

For example, the clamp cylinder could jam before the component was clamped.

If the cylinder did jam, the pressure would build up in the system and the sequence valve would open (passing). The stamp cylinder would then stamp the unclamped component.

To avoid this, a proof of position / limit valve is inserted after the sequence valve, with the cam roller set at the clamp cylinder.

Therefore, the clamp cylinder must reach full extension before the proof of position / limit valve will open (go passing) to allow air to reach the stamp cylinder.

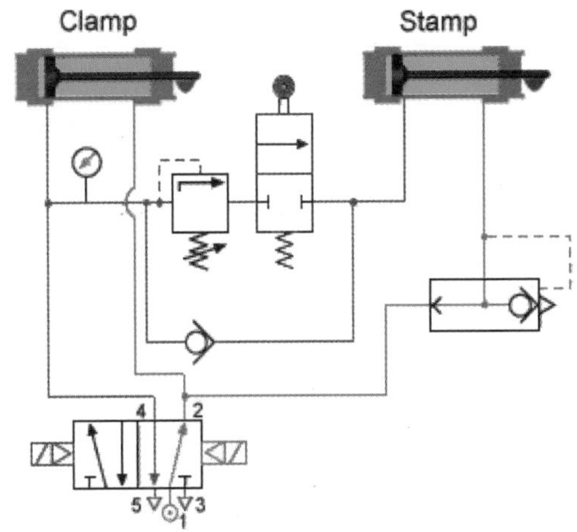

Sequential Control 1

A machine tool has two double acting pneumatic cylinders.

The sequence required to operate this machine tool correctly is:

- START
- A+(1.0)
- B+(2.0)
- A- (1.0)
- B- (2.0)

Both the numbering system and the letter system have been added to the circuit. The numbering system is shown in brackets. When cylinder 'A'

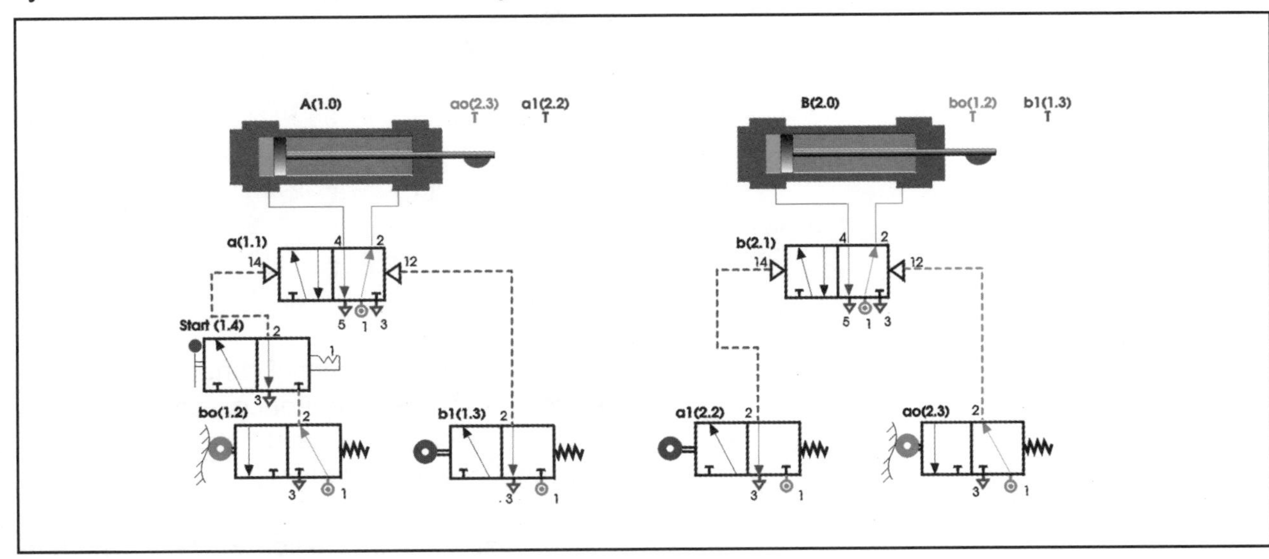

and cylinder 'B' are fully retracted, valves 'a0' and 'b0' are activated.

As the last sequence before the start sequence was 'B-' then 'b0' is placed in series as an 'AND' function with the start lever / detent valve.

When the start valve is activated, the directional control valve 'a' is operated and cylinder 'A ' extends.

This releases valve 'a0'. When 'A' is fully extended, valve 'a1' is activated, which, in turn, operates valve 'b' extending cylinder 'B'.

Valve 'b0' is released. When cylinder 'B' is fully extended, valve 'b1' is activated, operating valve 'a' and retracting cylinder 'A'. Valve 'a1' is released. When cylinder 'A' is fully retracted, valve 'a0' is activated, operating valve 'b' and retracting cylinder 'B'.

Valve 'b1' is released.

When cylinder 'B' is fully retracted, valve 'b0' is activated and if the start valve is still in its operated position, the cycle will start again.

This cycle is A+. B+. A-. B-.

Sequential Control 2

A machine tool has two double acting pneumatic cylinders which are required to follow the sequence.

- START
- A+(1.0)
- B+(2.0)
- B-(2.0)
- A-(1.0)

Note: Cylinder 2.0 (B) has to retract immediately after extending.

If the circuit from sequential control 1 was modified to give this new sequence, two pilot signals would be placed on valve 'b' at the same time. The sequence would stop.

In this situation the **group sequence** or **switched circuit** method of control is used.

The group signal method using a group control valve (G.C.V.) can be used to avoid trapped, opposing pilot signals in sequential control circuits.

Here a 5/2 pilot – pilot valve (G.C.V) has been added to the circuit. The output ports 4 and 2 are divided into two working groups / switch circuits, group I and group II. This method makes it impossible for both groups to have air on at the same time.

The start valve is connected to group I which has air supplied to it.

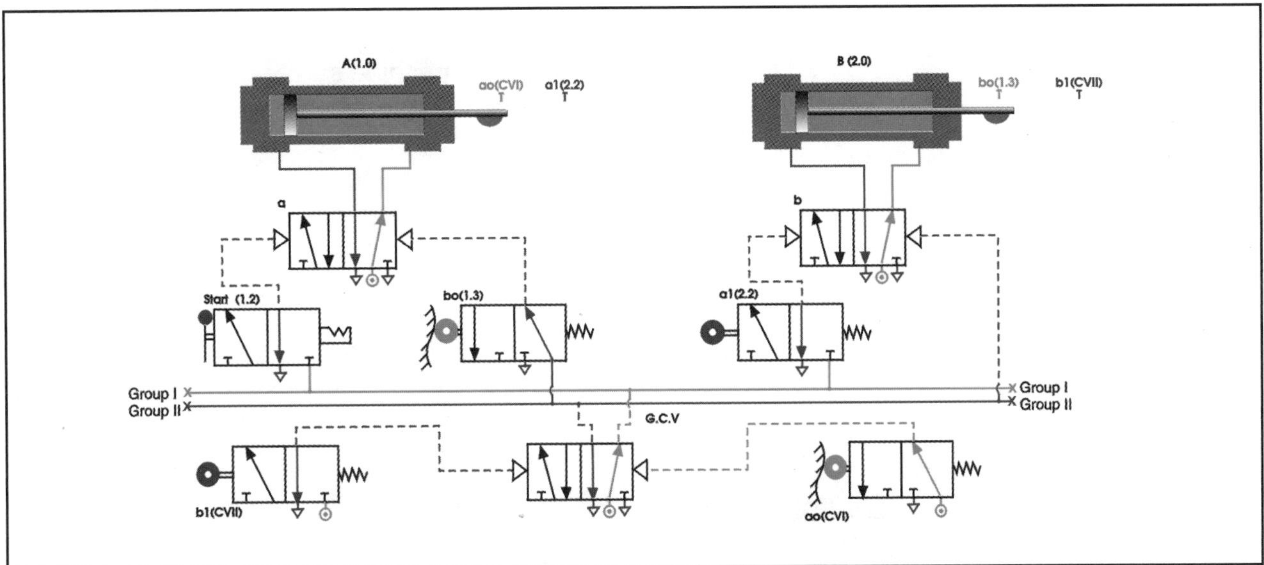

Directional control valve 'a' operates and cylinder 'A' extends.

Group I changeover valve 'a0' is released.

Limit switch 'a1' is reached, which extends cylinder 'B'. Limit switch 'b0' is released.

Cylinder 'B' operates group II changeover valve 'b1'. This changes the 5/2 group control valve (GCV) to pressurize line II. Line I is exhausted. Cylinder 'B' immediately retracts releasing 'b1'. Limit switch 'a1' is released.

On full retraction, cylinder 'A' actuates group I changeover valve 'a0'. This changes the group control valve 'GCV' back to pressurize line I and exhaust line II. If the start valve is still operated, the cycle continues.

Safety Circuits

Safety is of primary importance in any pneumatic circuit or system.

The forces generated within such systems could do great damage not only to machinery, but also to the people operating the system.

Circuits including safety features should be incorporated into the design of all circuits.

These ensure:
- Operator safety, by protecting them from moving parts and machinery.
- Plant or machine safety, so that damage cannot take place when the air is first switched on.
- That the machine **fails safe**, in an emergency such as sudden loss of air.

Two Hand Control Unit

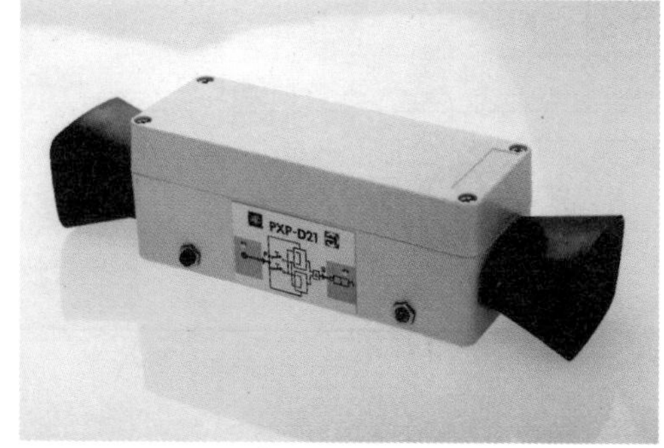

Two hand control units ensure that a system cannot be operated accidentally.

Before the machine can start, the operator must use **both** hands.

Normally two push buttons have to be operated **together** within a very short time space, usually 0.3 second.

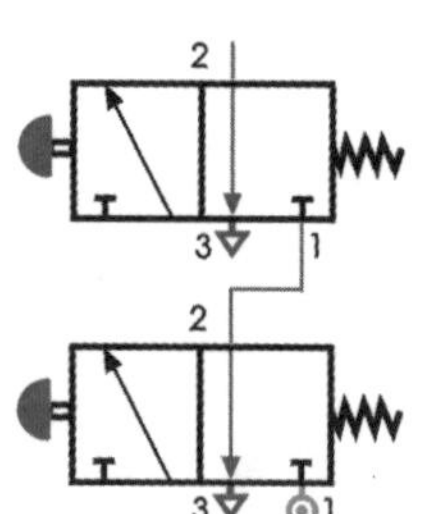

If this does not happen, the operator must release the push buttons to reset the valve before operating again.

Two valves, e.g. 3/2 normally closed / non passing push button valves in series or connected to an "AND" logic valve are not acceptable as one or both of the actuators could be fastened or wedged down and the machine will still operate.

Guard Unit

Another mechanism to minimize the risk of accidentally activating a machine is the **guard**.

This is attached to a safety circuit, which renders the machine inoperable when the guard is not in place. Thus the machine can only operate when the guard is in place, thereby isolating the operator from any moving parts.

Slow Pressure Initialization

In most pneumatic systems, air can be turned on via a stop / shutoff valve. The pressure then rises very quickly. In certain applications this could be very dangerous.

For example, if a pneumatic cylinder has been left in an extended position, it may retract at a high velocity. This is dangerous for personnel and could damage the components or machine. To stop this from happening, a "soft start" valve is placed on the inlet of the machine.

When the air is turned on, the pressure builds up gradually and the problem can be spotted in time.

Fail Safe Circuits

Consideration must be given to questions such as **what would happen if the air failed?**

Or, **what would happen if the emergency stop button was pressed?**

If the air failed, cylinders with loads may come crashing down, damaging the machine or causing serious injury.

If the emergency stop button was pressed, the circuit may be in the wrong sequence when started again and cause injury or damage.

Directional control valves play an important role here. They are generally 5/3 valves with a mid position.

Mid position valves allow air to be locked into a system, as shown here, or release all pressure by ports '4' and '2' of the valve being connected to exhaust ports '5' and '3'.

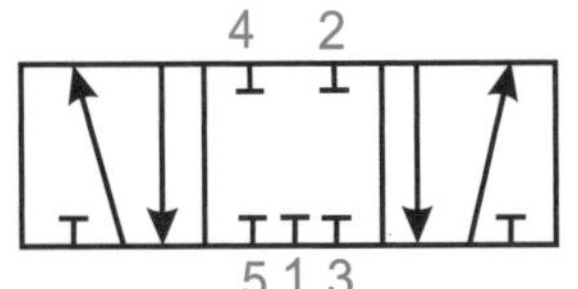

Incorporating this type of valve with other combinations will help ensure that a system fails safe.

Summary

Design Principles

Circuit diagrams, using ISO symbols and either letter or number identification, as a crucial part of pneumatic technology.

Use of the appropriate symbols and nomenclature will ensure that it is clear which component is controlling the circuit and at the appropriate time.

Single Acting Cylinder Circuits

3/2 valves are commonly used to control these circuits.

Cylinder velocity is affected by the inclusion of a flow control valve in the circuit.

Double Acting Cylinder Circuits

52 and 4/2 directional control valves are used to control double acting cylinders and are used in basic circuits.

Variations in the velocity of cylinder strokes can also be achieved by flow control valves.

Circuits can be controlled remotely by incorporating signal valves (devices) and shuttle valves.

Automatic control of circuits can be achieved using signal or proof of position valves.

Time delay circuits can be devised using time delay valves (components).

Pressure sequence valves can be used to ensure that cylinders move in the correct sequence or order and maintain a pressure in the circuit.

Safety Circuits

Safety circuits must be incorporated into the design of all circuits. The Two Hand Start and Guard circuits ensure that a machine is not switched on accidentally.

Slow pressure initialization ensures that pressure does not rise too quickly in a pneumatic circuit. It is important that all circuits should fail safely to avoid damage to equipment and injury to personnel.

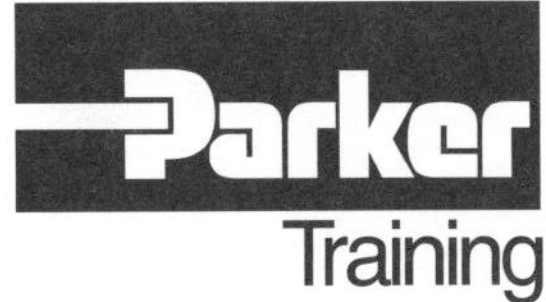

Module 5

Electro Pneumatics

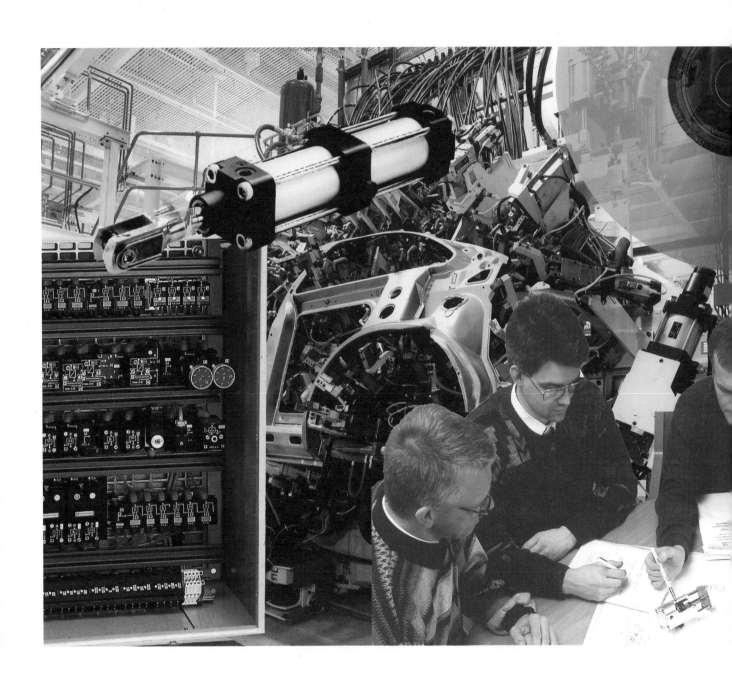

Contents

Introduction

A great number of pneumatic valves are being controlled by electrical / electronic signals in industrial machinery today. By using electrical devices this enables machines to be controlled more accurately and are easily changed by using programmable logic controllers PLCs

Objectives

In this section the following will be examined:

- Basic Electrical Principles
- Ladder diagrams / switches
- Solenoid Valves
- Relays
- Symbols
- Electro pneumatic circuits for single acting cylinders
- Electro pneumatic circuits for double acting cylinders
- PLCs

Basic Electrical Principles

In this introduction to electro-pneumatic circuitry the full electrical technology is a subject in its own right. Simplified circuit drawings are used together with basic nomenclature to give an overview of the subject.

The electrical supply, known as the source, can be produced from a battery or common electrical power.

Switches are used as a means of control.

The load can be a light, solenoid, motor, etc.

Opposite is shown a single solenoid valve.

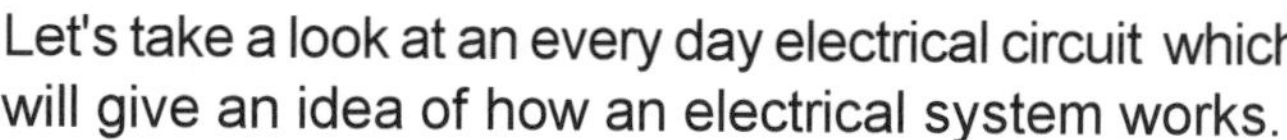

Let's take a look at an every day electrical circuit which will give an idea of how an electrical system works.

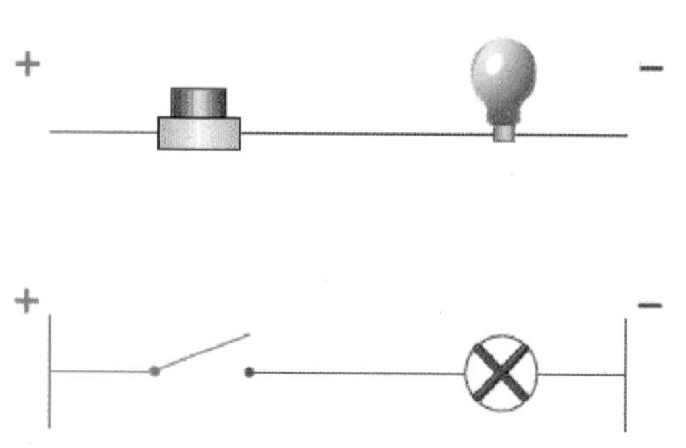

Ladder Diagram

Here is a light which is shown symbolically by a cross within a circle.

Next to it is a switch to operate the light.

Finally the switch and light have to be wired together and connected to an electrical power source.

By using conventional electrical circuit theory, current travels from +ve to -ve. This forms the basis of a ladder diagram. When the switch is operated the light comes on.

A push button switch has to be pressed continually to keep the light on whereas a 2 position toggle switch will stay in the operated position.

Electrical Component and Switches

To establish the position of an air cylinder a variety of electrical switches are available. These switches include limit switches, proximity switches, pressure switches and magnetic reed switches. Switches are also required to give a start signal.

The switch is a mechanical device that either opens (non passing) or closes (passing) sets of contacts inside the body of the switch.

A standard switch will have possibly only one normally open (non passing) contact or one normally closed (passing) contact.

However there are also multiple contact switches that can be used.

The contacts in the switch change state from either open (non passing) to closed (passing) or vice versa, when the switch is operated.

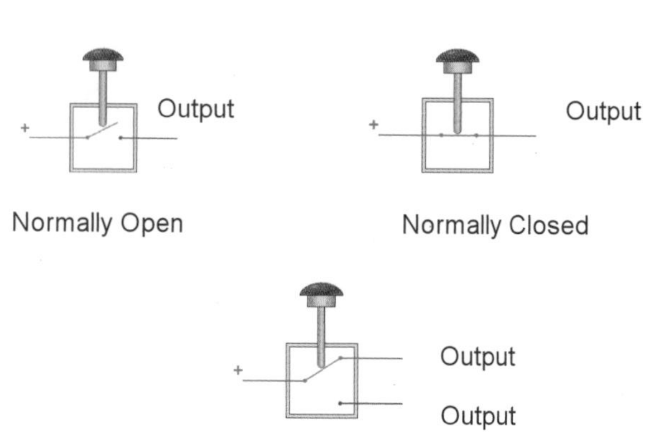

Pushbutton switches

This actuator is normally a green or red colored button that is operated manually, by hand or finger, to change the state of the contacts.

Emergency stop buttons are red, usually very large and easy to operate.

Toggle Switch

This switch is operated by hand. It can be left in either the "on" or "off" position by a detent mechanism.

It can be returned to its original position by a spring or by a 3 position switch by way of a centering device.

Limit Switches

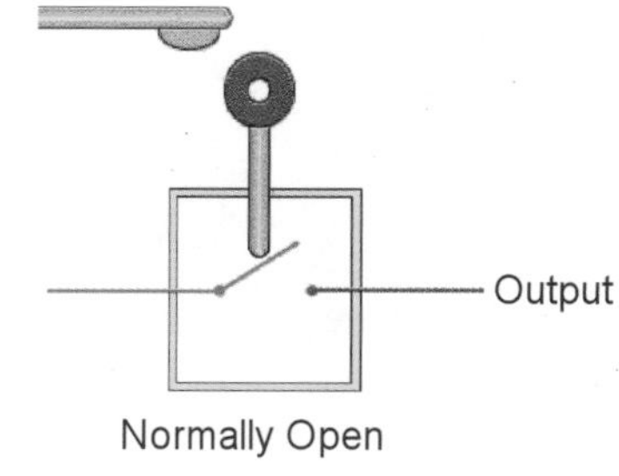

These valve actuators are used to establish the position of cylinders, guards and equipment to give feedback to the electrical circuit. They can be a cam roller lever, one way trip lever, plunger or ball.

Pressure Sensors

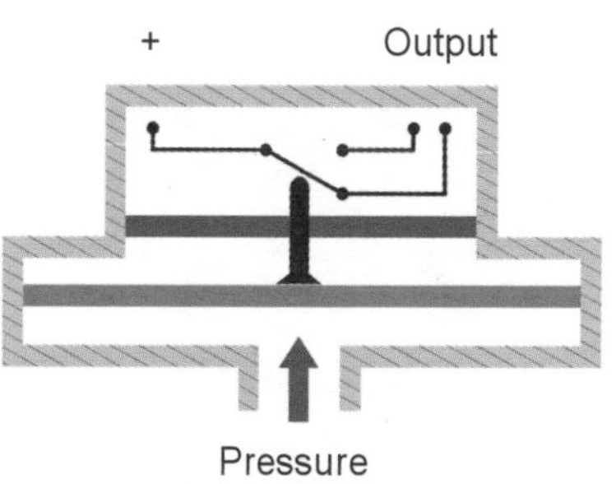

This device senses the air pressure to operate the switch contacts.

Due to the area of the diaphragm, any air pressure applied to it is amplified, giving a fast response.

These devices are usually adjustable to switch at a desired pressure.

Vacuum Switch

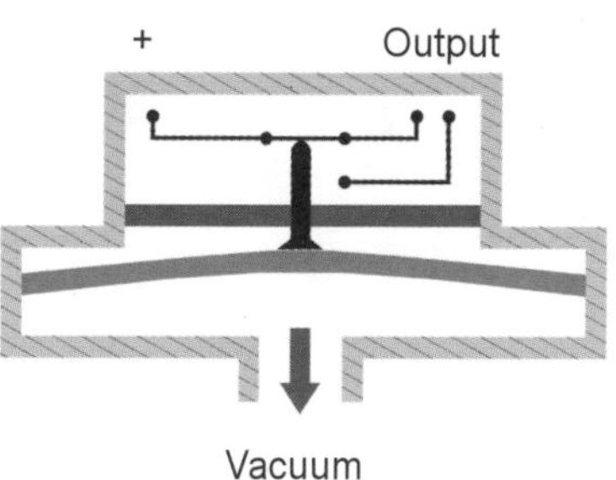

This actuator, although looking similar to the pressure actuator, works in the opposite way.

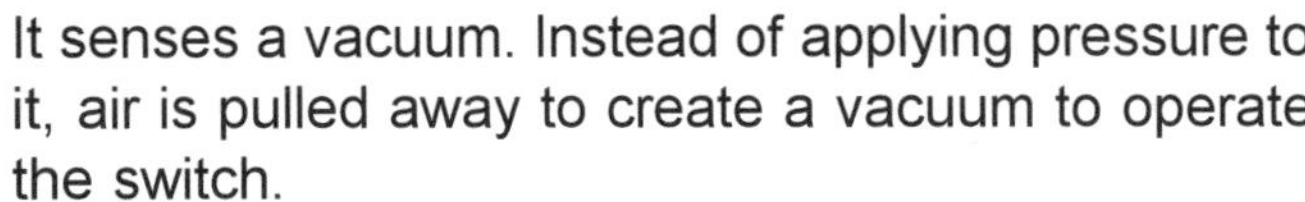

It senses a vacuum. Instead of applying pressure to it, air is pulled away to create a vacuum to operate the switch.

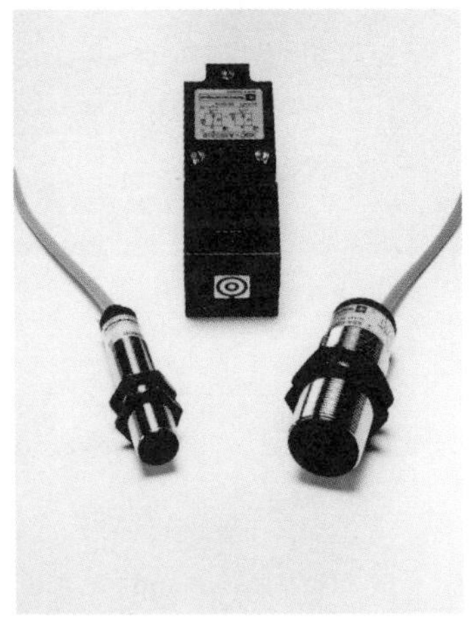

Proximity Sensor

Proximity switches work by not making contact with an object but by sensing that the object is within its proximity.

This type of switch can be either magnetic (recognition of ferrous metal) to sense that an object is close to it, or a capacitive switch which uses electronics to sense that an object is very close.

Magnetic Reed Switches

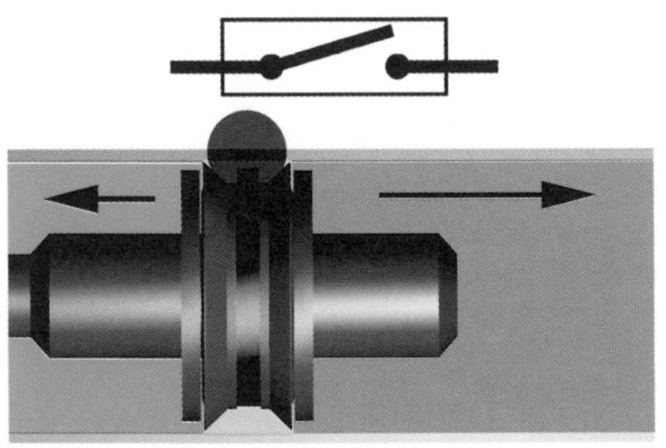

Magnetic reed switches are used to establish the position of the piston within the air cylinder and are usually adjustable. They can be moved along the length of the cylinder body to any desired position (i.e. where the piston position needs to be signalled) or in the case of a semi rotary actuator at the rotated position.

Optical Sensor

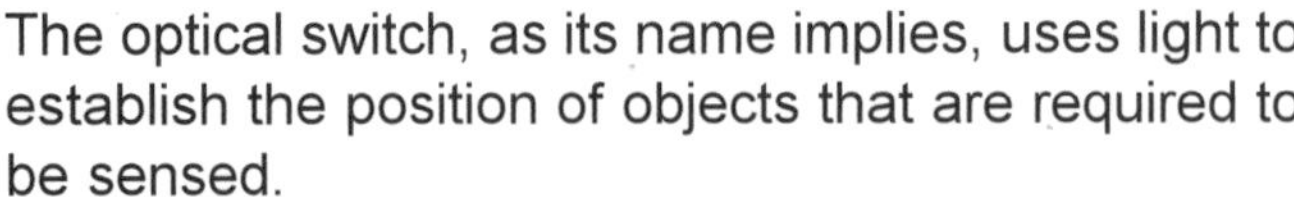

The optical switch, as its name implies, uses light to establish the position of objects that are required to be sensed.

The **beam type** has a sender or light source and a receiver.

The light source shines a light beam into the receiver. When the light beam is broken by an object, the state of the output from the receiver changes.

Reflective Type

This type of device has both a light source and receiver incorporated into the same unit.

The light source is bounced off a reflector on the object to be sensed and back into the receiver. Once again when the light beam is broken, the device changes state.

The light source on both of these devices is usually infrared.

Solenoid

The solenoid is an electrical device that operates the valve.

The solenoid creates an electromagnetic field when energized. This lifts a small poppet which allows air to operate the valve.

This then moves the spool in the main valve.

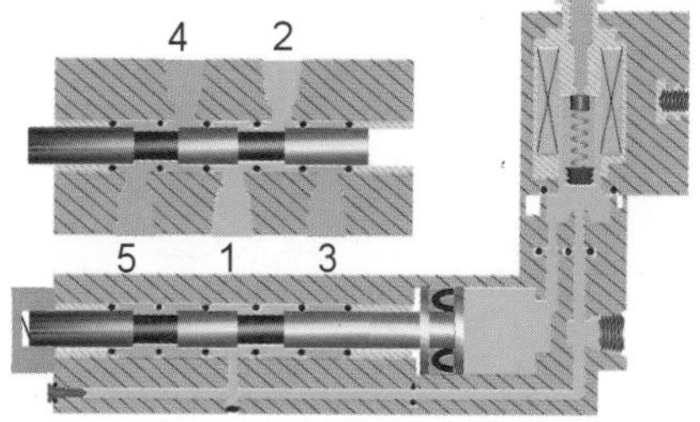

By using compressed air to move the main air valve, very little electrical energy is required. If the valve spool was connected direct to an electromagnetic solenoid, the solenoid would be considerably larger, and use much more electrical energy.

Relays

In small low current electrical circuits push button switches, roller switches and toggle switches can operate a solenoid direct.

Switches, therefore, provide a control signal and relays are used where high electrical loads are required.

The relay acts as an interface between two electrical circuits.

Relays consist of a coil, similar to a solenoid connected to switches which can be a combination of normally closed (passing) contacts.

Relays enable one circuit to operate another with no electrical connections between them. Therefore a low voltage, low current circuit can operate high voltage high current circuitry.

Standard electrical symbols

Here we see the standard symbols used in electrical circuitry.

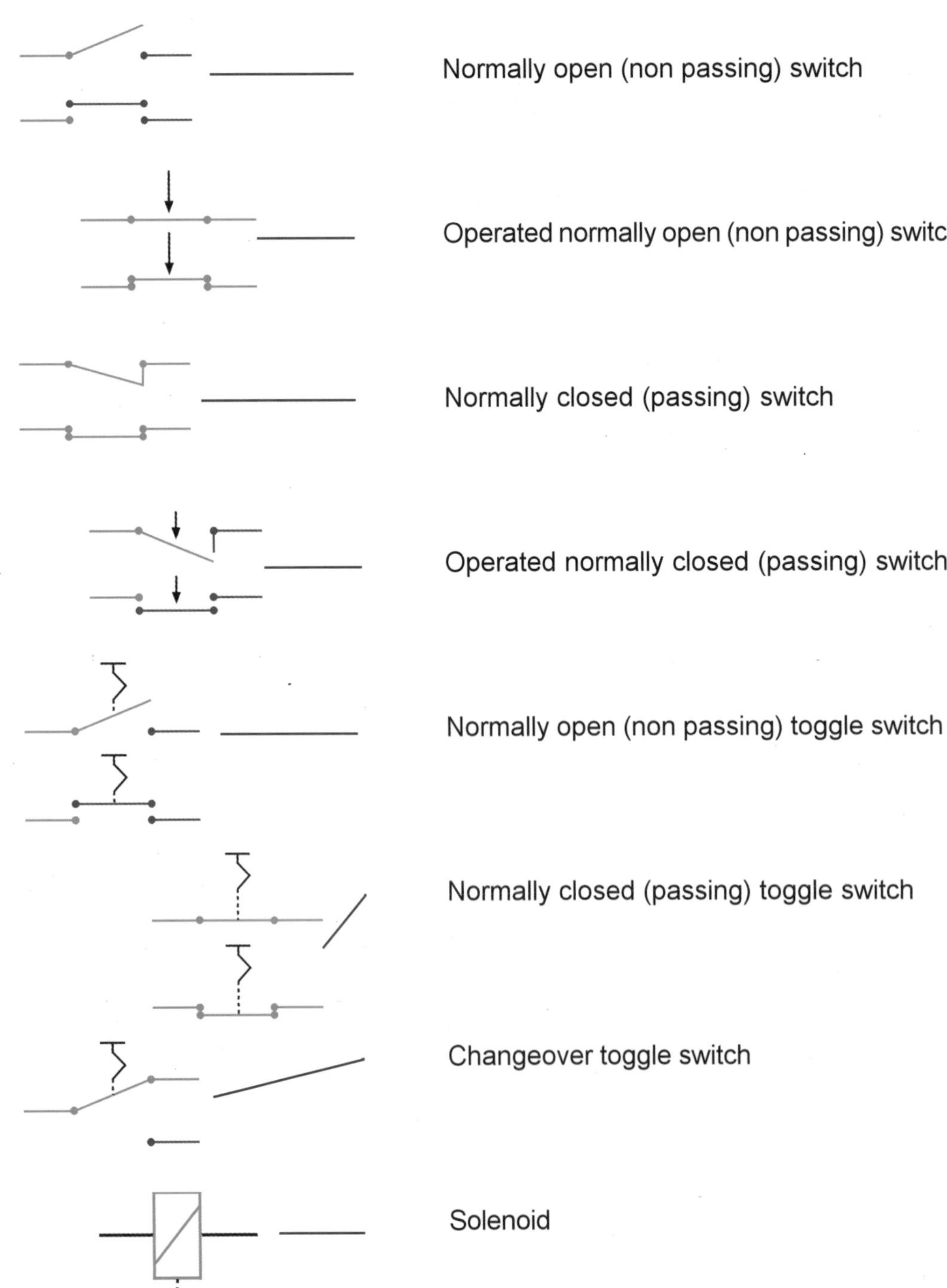

- Relay

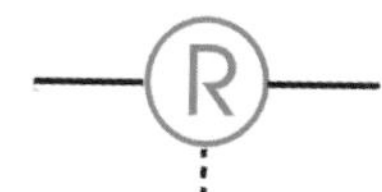

Basic Electrical Circuits

Single Acting Cylinder Circuit

The push button electrical valve in Fig. 1 is operated, which in turn energizes (switches on) the solenoid coil. The pneumatic valve operates and the cylinder extends.

When the push button is released the solenoid de-energizes (switches off) and the pneumatic valve returns to its original position and the cylinder retracts.

The push button can be replaced by a lockdown / detent lever, (Fig. 2) to keep the solenoid energized and the cylinder extended.

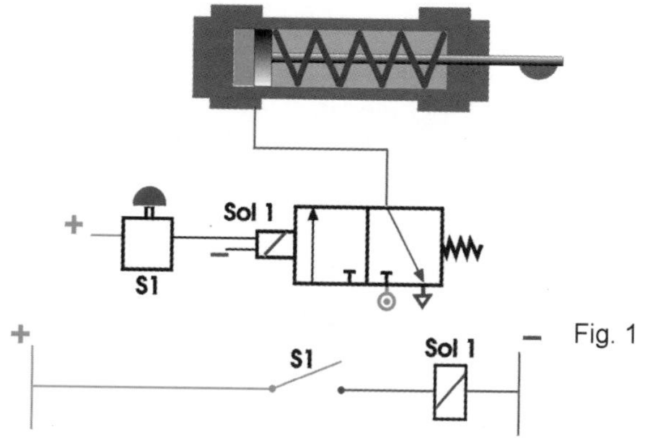

Fig. 1

Single Acting Cylinder Circuit 'OR' Function

In circuit Fig. 3 a two-position toggle switch is added in parallel with the push button switch.

This allows the operator to energize the solenoid by two methods.

Method one means the push button has to be kept depressed. Method two allows the switch to be locked; this keeps the solenoid energized and the cylinder extended until the switch is reset to its initial position.

This type of circuit is an 'or' circuit.

Switch 1 'or' switch 2 will operate the cylinder.

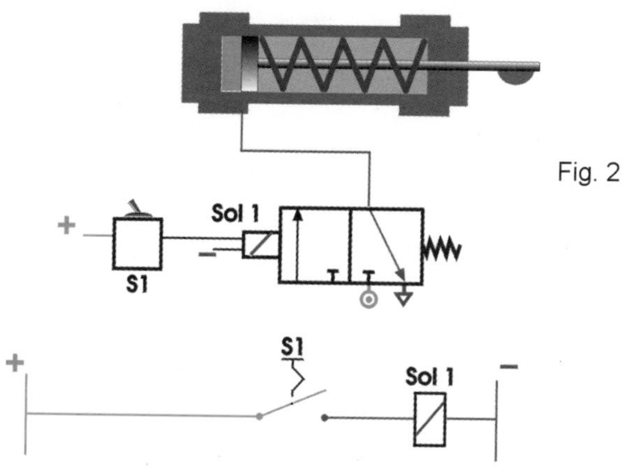

Fig. 2

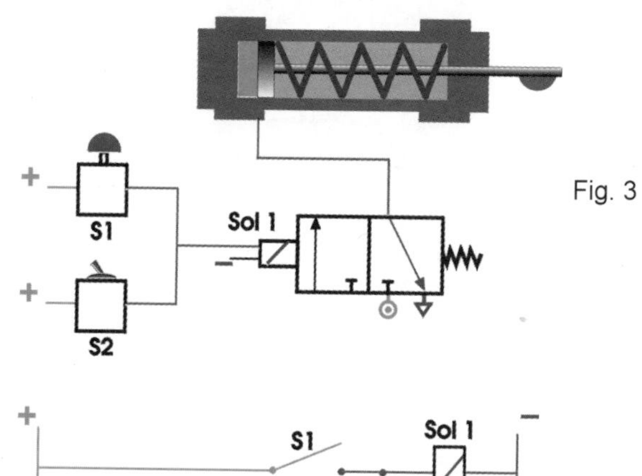

Fig. 3

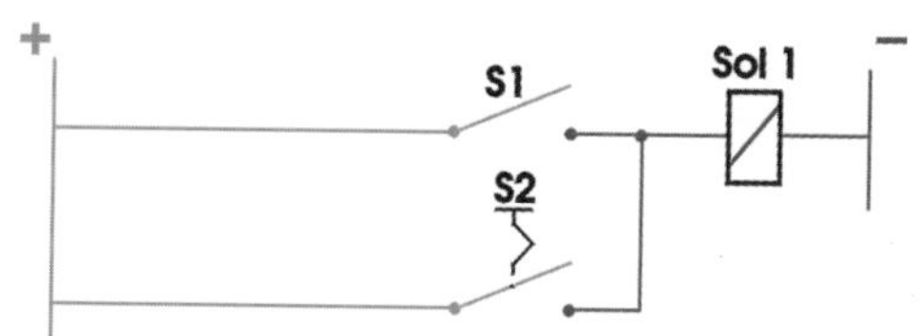

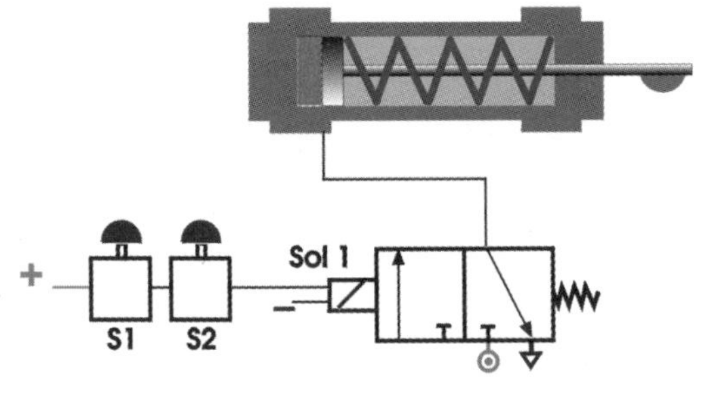

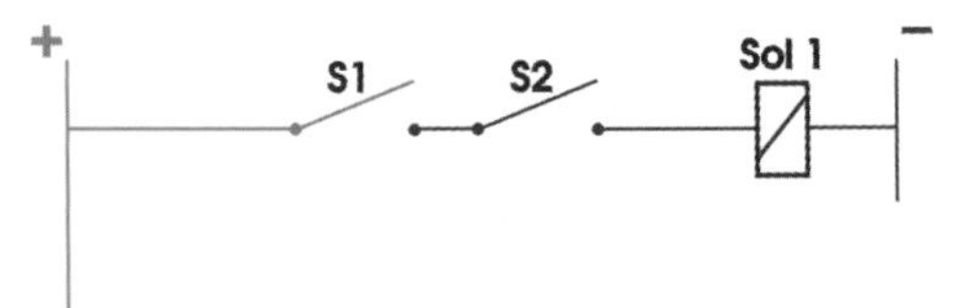

Single Acting Cylinder Circuit 'AND' Function

In this circuit two electrical switches are placed in series.

Both switch 1 'and' switch 2 must be operated before the cylinder will operate.

This is called an 'and' circuit.

Double Acting Cylinder Circuit

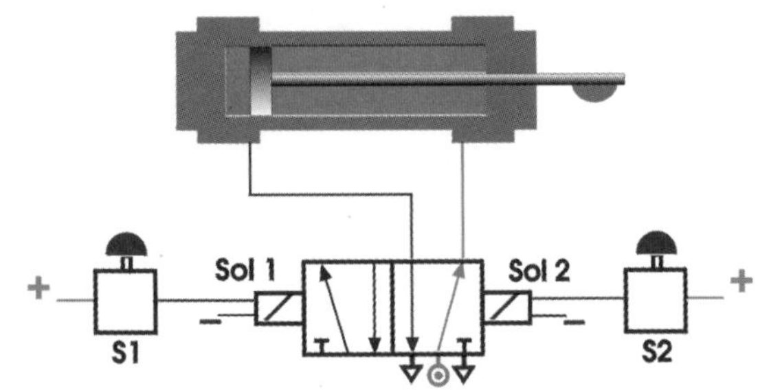

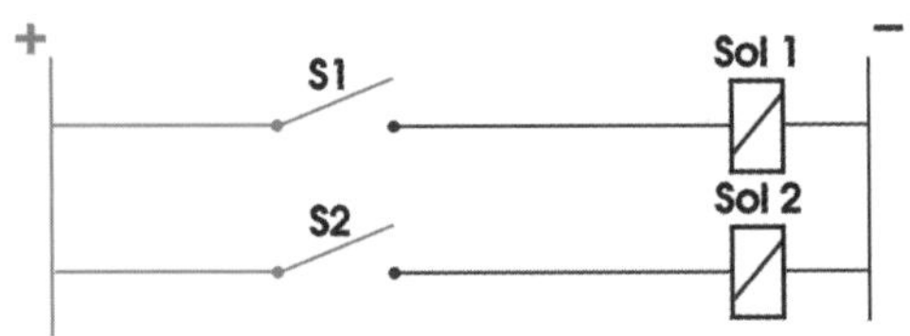

This circuit uses a double solenoid 5/2 pneumatic directional control valve.

The electrical push button is pressed once and then released. The left hand solenoid is energized momentarily and the **bi-stable** or **two position** valve changes over. The cylinder extends.

Even though the solenoid power is off the valve will remain in this position, due to its construction, until the second push button is operated only for a short period.

The valve changes over and the cylinder retracts.

Double Acting Cylinder Circuit Semi Automatic

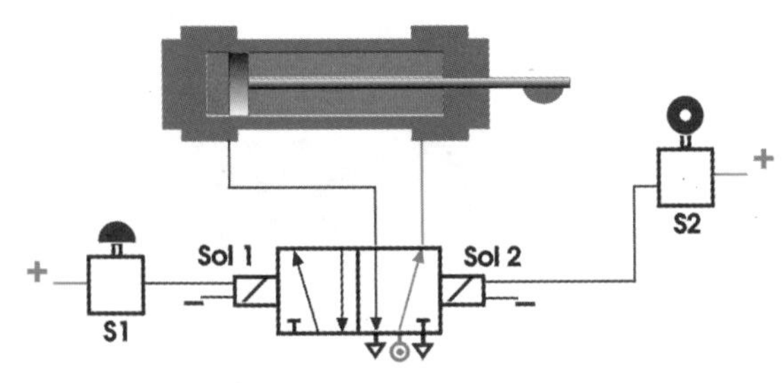

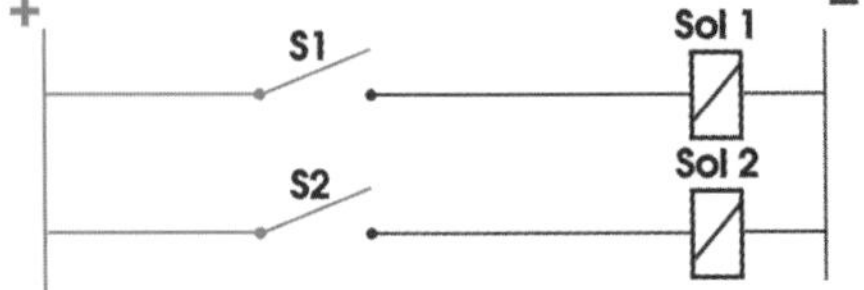

In this circuit the retract push button switch from the previous circuit is replaced by a cam roller type limit switch. This is operated by a cam on the extension stroke of the cylinder.

When the extension push button switch is operated momentarily the solenoid valve extends the cylinder.

The cam operates the cam roller limit switch automatically and the cylinder retracts.
If the push button switch is not released before the cam hits the cam roller limit switch, the cylinder will continue to the end of its stroke and stop.

This is due to the double solenoid valve being bi-stable. It will stay in its actuated position even if both solenoids are energized.

By moving the cam roller switch towards the cylinder this will shorten the usable stroke length.

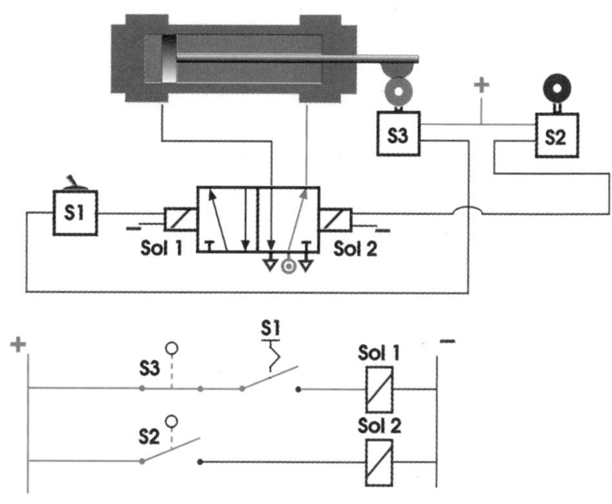

Double Acting Cylinder Circuit Fully Automated

By placing a second cam roller limit switch 'S3' on the retraction stroke of the cylinder, the signal from this switch will automate the start sequence.

In this case the push button "start" switch can be changed to a toggle switch which has a latch (detent) position.

This creates a continuous cycle and the cylinder will reciprocate (extend and retract) until the toggle switch is reset to its initial condition.

The toggle switch S1 and the cam roller valve S3 produce an "and" function.

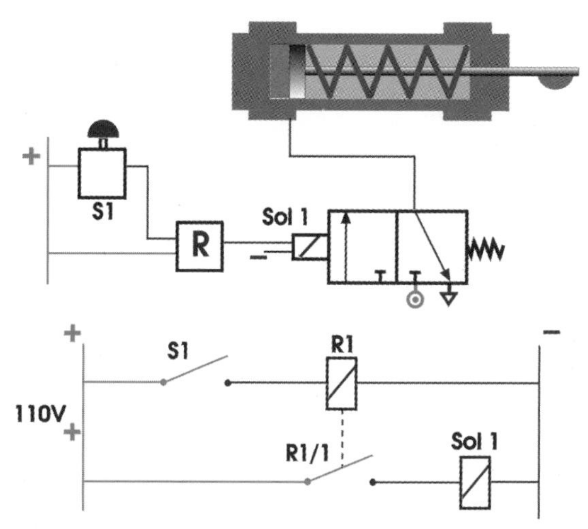

Monostable Circuit

When the push button is operated the relay coil energizes and the contacts change over.

If the electrical output of the relay is connected to a solenoid valve, this would then energize the valve and operate the cylinder.

When the push button is released the relay returns to its original position as the coil de-energizes (switches off).

This in turn de-energizes the solenoid valve and the cylinder retracts.

This is known as a Monostable Circuit.

In certain electrical circuits, low voltage (12 volt or 24 volt) is used to generate the signals to the relay. The main contacts of the relay can be connected to a higher voltage to operate solenoid valves or other output devices where electrical loads may be large.

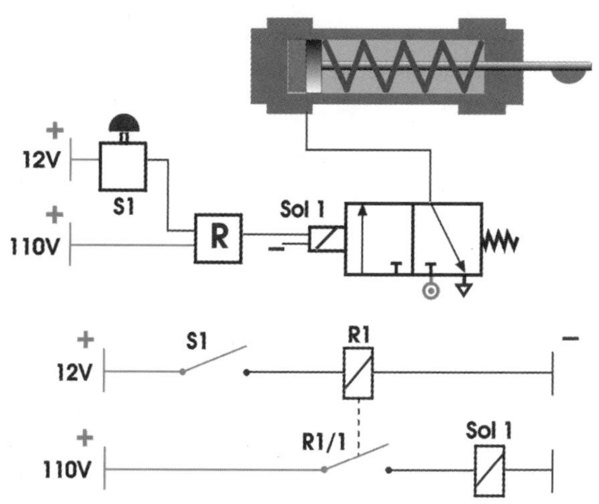

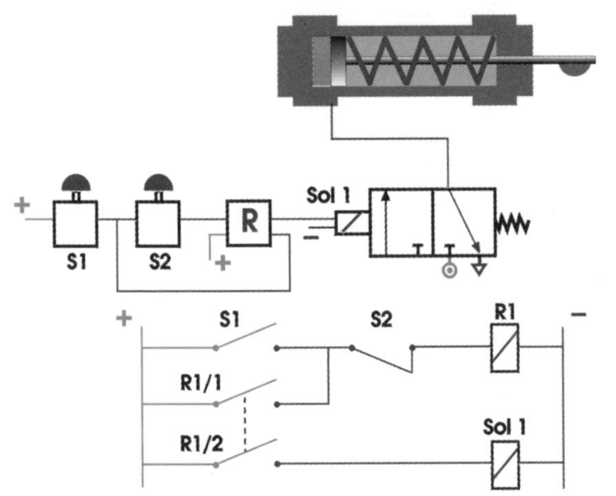

Bi-stable Circuit / Latching Circuit

The relay can also be used as a latching (detent) switch to maintain the signal to the solenoid valve when push button 'S1' is released.

Push button 'S2' is a normally closed (passing) switch.

When relay 'R1' is energized contacts 'R1/1' latches the circuit and contacts 'R1/2' energizes solenoid 'Sol 1'. Push button 'S1' can now be released and the cylinder will remain extended.

To unlatch the relay "normally closed" (passing) switch 'S2' is operated.

By operating this switch the line is disconnected and the relay coil de-energizes. This is known as a bi-stable latching circuit and is useful when using a single solenoid valve.

Sequential Control - 2 Cylinders

Here are 2 cylinders, 1.0 (A) and 2.0 (B).

The sequence required is: start, 1.0 (A) +, 2.0 (B) +, 1.0 (A) -, 2.0 (B) - stop or repeat.

The limit / position switches are S1, S2, S3 S4 and start push button PB1.

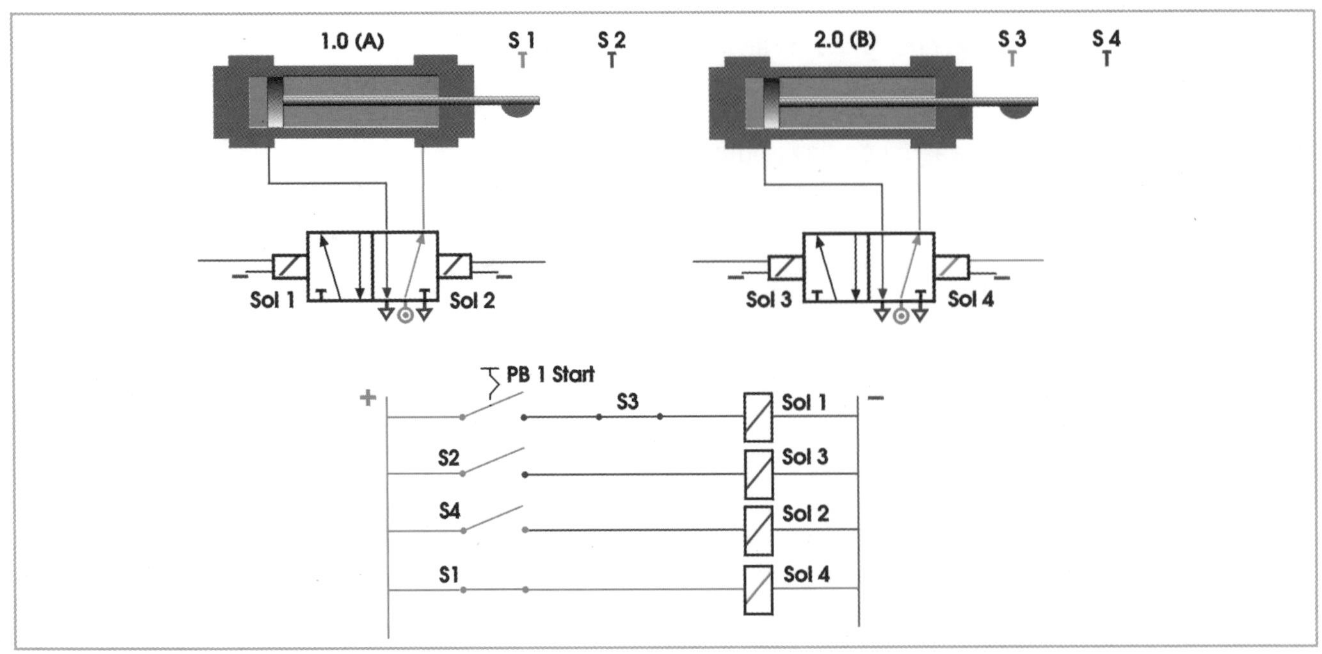

The solenoids are marked Sol 1, Sol 2, Sol 3, Sol 4.

Limit switch 'S3' is already in its closed / passing position and when PB1 is operated, solenoid 'Sol 1' is energized.

Cylinder 1.0(A) extends.

Limit switch 'S1' opens, (is released) and goes non-passing when cylinder 1.0(A) extends, de-energizing 'Sol 4'. 'S2' is reached and operated (made) by the cylinder energizing 'Sol 3'. Cylinder 2.0(B) extends releasing switch 'S3' and de-energizing 'Sol 1'. 'S4' is reached (made) by the cylinder, energizing 'Sol 2'. Cylinder 1.0(A) retracts.

'S2' is released (goes non-passing) as cylinder 1.0(A) retracts, de-energizing 'Sol 3'.

'S1' is closed (goes passing) and energizes 'Sol 4', cylinder 2.0(B) retracts releasing 'S4' (goes non passing) and de-energizing 'Sol 2'. When 'S3' is made by cylinder 2.0(B) the cycle is complete.

If PB1 remains in its operated state, the cycle will continue.

Sequential Control - 2 Cylinders (Cascade)

In this sequential control circuit the cylinder cycle is:

1.0 (A) + 2.0 (B) + 2.0 (B) - 1.0 (A) -

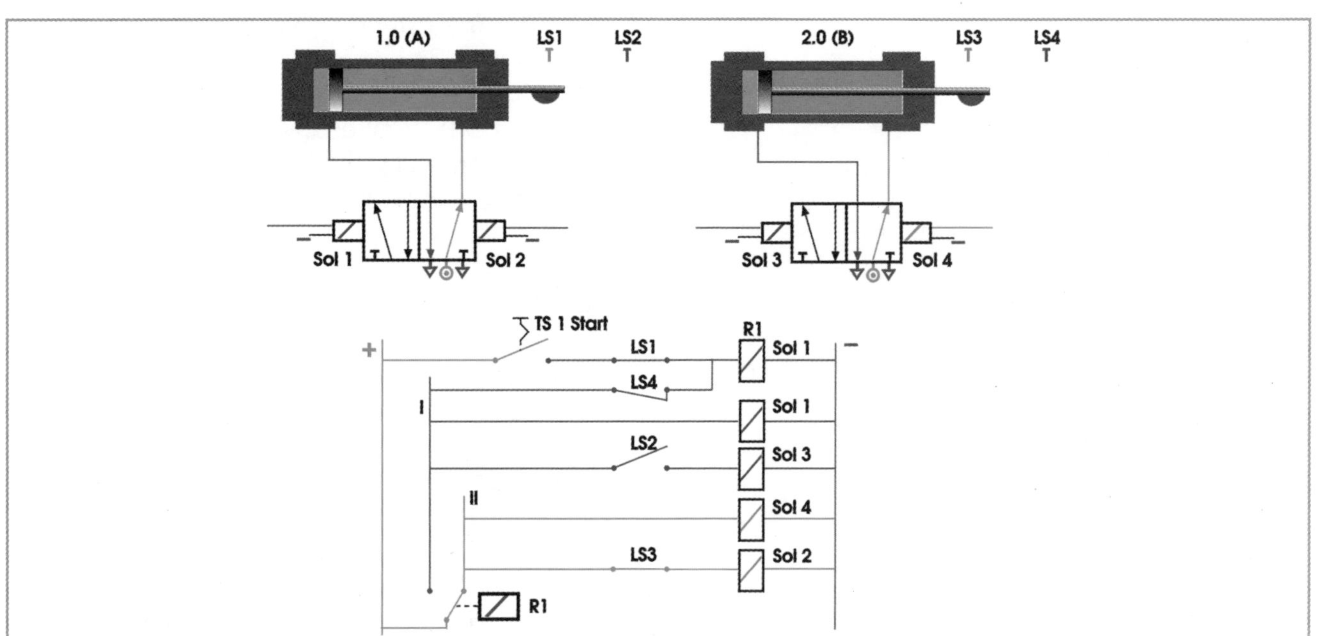

When the same cylinder, in this case 2.0 (B) changes from extension (+) to immediate retraction (-) the opposing solenoid Sol 3 is still energized.

Therefore when S4 is energized (made) S3 must be de-energized to allow the pneumatic valve to change position.

Therefore the electrical equivalent of the 'cascade' system described in Module 4 must be used.

In this circuit the switches will operate the solenoid valves directly for ease of understanding.

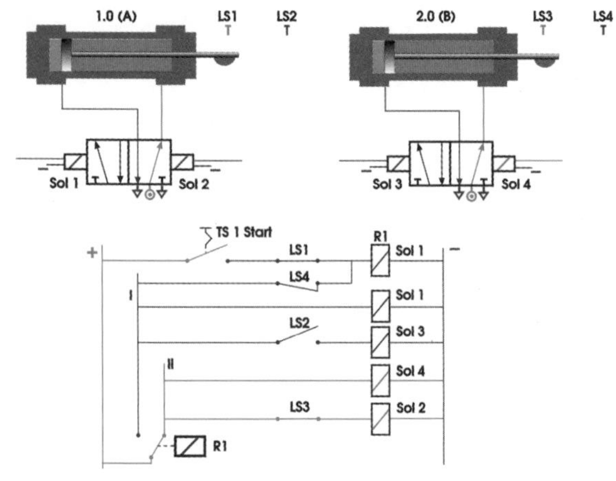

Relay R1 is incorporated into the circuit which acts as a changeover switch.

When the start switch is operated electrical current flows through limit switch LS1 energizing the relay R1.

The relay R1 contacts switch over putting power onto the line 1.

LS4 being a normally closed (passing) switch latches the relay as described previously in the bi-stable circuit / latching circuit section.

Solenoid valve Sol 1 is energized which extends cylinder 1.0 (A). Limit switch LS1 is released but does not affect the circuit at this time.

Cylinder 1.0 (A) operates (makes) switch LS2, energizing solenoid Sol 3.

Cylinder 2.0 (B) extends disconnecting (releasing) switch LS3.

As cylinder 2.0 (B) makes switch LS4, this normally closed (passing) valve now disconnects (releases) and unlatches relay R1.

This switches the contacts and powers up line II. Line I is now de-energized.

Solenoid Sol 4 automatically energizes retracting cylinder 2.0 (B).

As the cylinder moves back switch LS4 is released bringing it into the normally closed (passing) position.

When cylinder 2.0 (B) is fully retracted switch LS3 is operated (made) energizing solenoid Sol 2.

Cylinder 1.0 (A) retracts.

Switch LS1 is made on full retraction and if the toggle switch is also actuated the cycle will start again.

PLCs

In today's high tech industries electrical and electronic circuits are being replaced by Programmable Logic Controllers - PLCs.

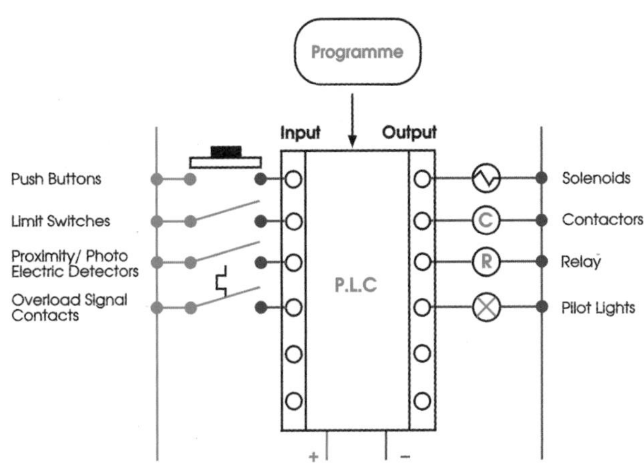

The PLC takes inputs from various sources including switches, sensors and detectors.

The PLC then analyzes these inputs and processes them in accordance with their software program requirements.

The PLC then signals to output devices and drivers such as solenoids, contactors, relays and indicators.

These units are easily programmed and are very flexible and versatile.

The traditional method of PLC connections is where each wire has to be physically connected, making it very time consuming.

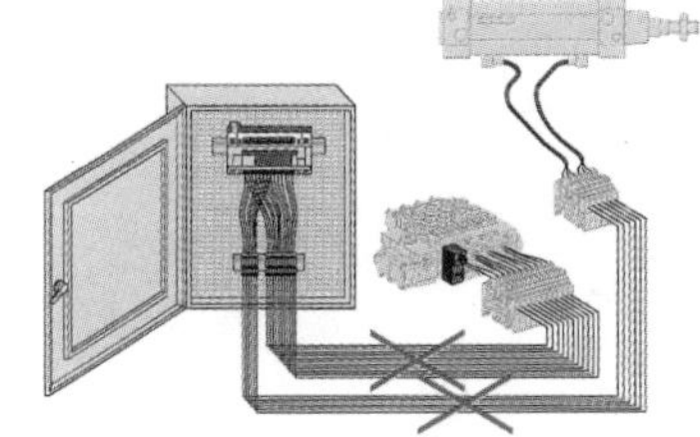

A simplified set up is the direct connection of a PLC, field bus or a special terminal block with a multiwire cable.

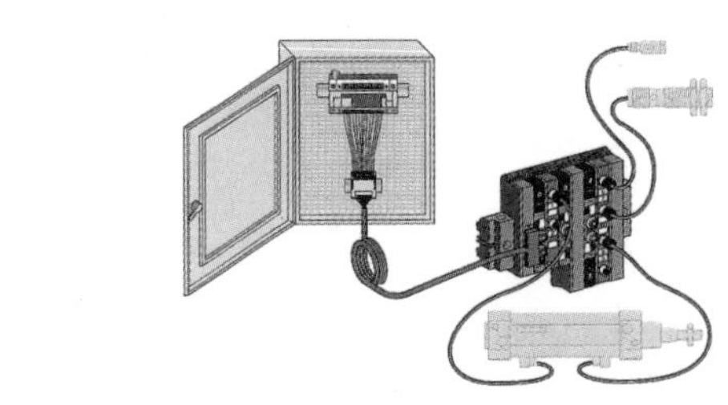

The 'Open System' uses a serial interface (open field bus) which dramatically reduces the number of wires for the inputs and outputs.

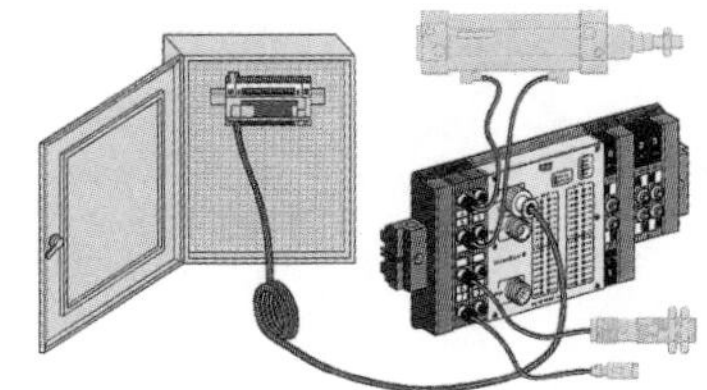

Summary

Basic electrical components, include

- Pushbutton switches
- Toggle switches
- Cam roller lever switches
- One way lever switches
- Plunger switch
- Ball switch

Sensors can be:

- Inductive (magnetic)
- Capacitive
- Optical

Ladder diagrams incorporating electrical symbols are used to show the sequential flow in a circuit.

Switches are used in a variety of combinations in electropneumatic circuits.

The output device in an electrical circuit is usually a solenoid or relay.

Solenoids generally operate pneumatic valves. Relays can operate solenoids, motors and other high current equipment.

Relays can be used in electropneumatic circuits to produce the electrical equivalent of the pneumatic cascade system.

PLCs are used widely in engineering as they are flexible and versatile.

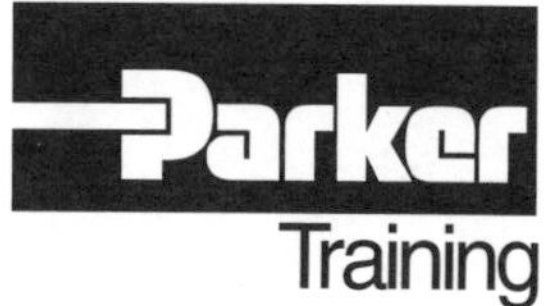

Module 6

Logic Valves & Circuits

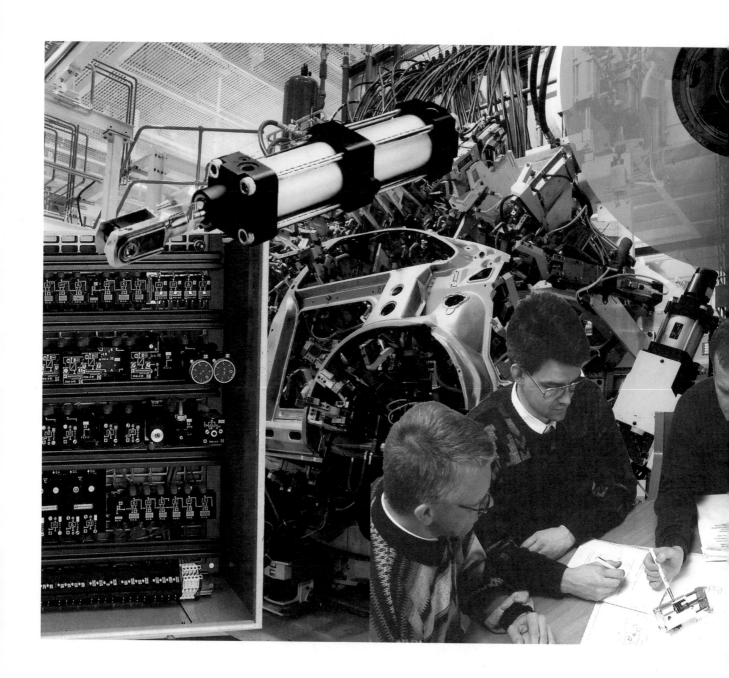

Contents

Logic Valves and Circuits

Objectives

In this section we will be examining:

- Pneumatic sensors
- Logic valves
- Logic sequential control

Overview

Most logic systems work in Binary.

When there is an "output" or an element is "on", this is called a Logic 1.

When there is no output or an element is "off" this is a Logic 0.

For example when a light is switched "on" this is a Logic 1.

When it is turned "off" this is a Logic 0.

Logic 1s and 0s can be combined to give different control functions.

Logic valves typically work between 3 to 8 bar (45 - 120 psi) pressure range.

They are very reliable with up to 100 million cycles achievable.

Due to their compactness the operating time is very fast at 2 - 3 milliseconds.

Logic equipment can be connected to a normal lubricated or unlubricated air supply.

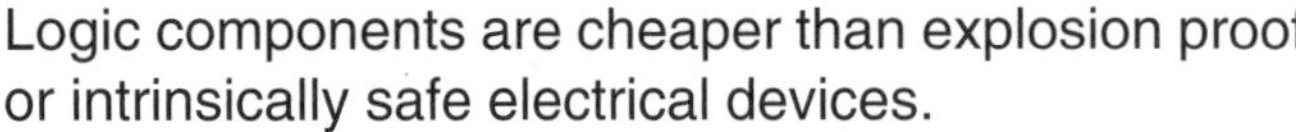

Logic components are cheaper than explosion proof or intrinsically safe electrical devices.

They are used where electrical / electronic equipment have a potential to cause sparks and may create an unsafe and dangerous situation.

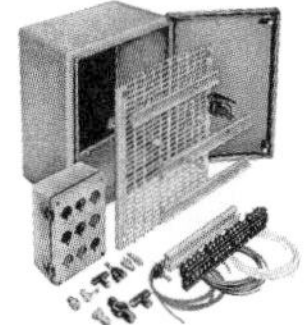

Hazardous environments such as industries handling; gases, aerosols and munitions, make logic circuitry ideal.

Industry uses logic for many applications because most actuators are pneumatic and sensing is simple. Welding or high 'amp' equipment can cause problems with electrical systems, making pneumatic logic ideal where this type of equipment is used.

Signal Valves, Sensors and Timers

Signal Valves

Most signal valves or manual pilot devices are miniature pneumatic valves which have a variety of operators or actuators.

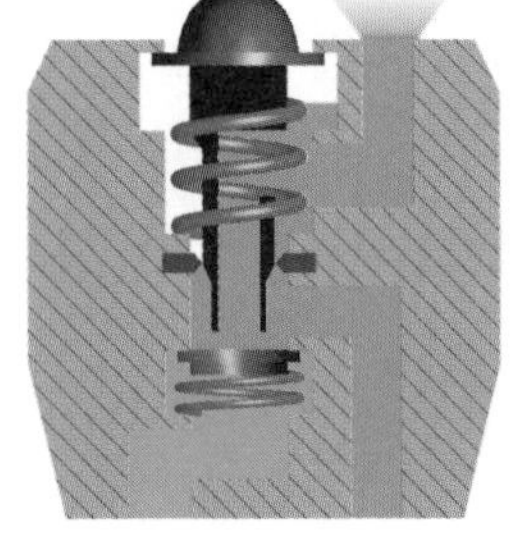

Valves generally have instant push lock connections.

The valve is usually of the poppet type shown here.

When the valve is actuated, the exhaust orifice in the plunger is closed (blocked) before the main line is open.

When the valve is released, the main line is closed (blocked) by the poppet before the opening of the exhaust port.

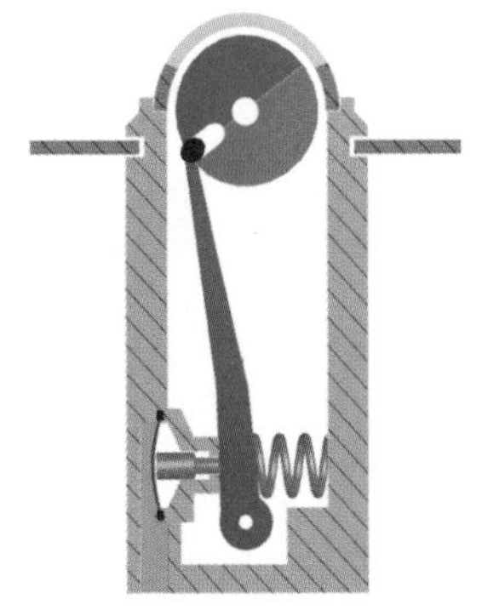

Indicators

Indicators are ideal when fault finding in pneumatic systems. They show when air is present by a change of color behind the lens. Indicators are small and simple in operation. Air operates the small diaphragm which moves the lever. This in turn rotates the colored disc showing that air is present in the line.

Sensors

Position sensors in general have some form of mechanical actuation. These range from the cam roller lever, plunger or button valve, the very sensitive whisker valve to the Pressure Threshold Detection sensor which mounts in the cylinder port as shown here.

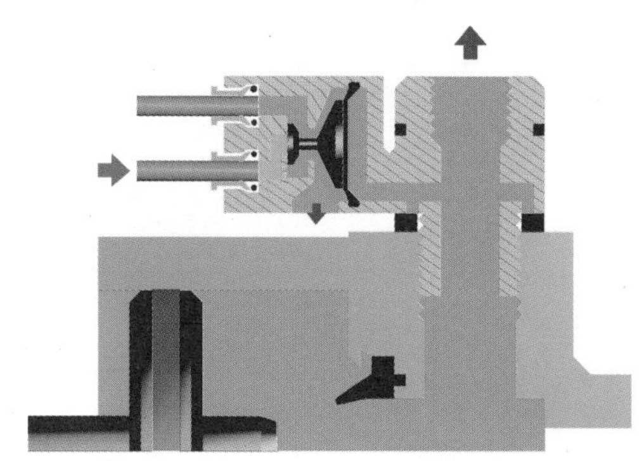

An end of stroke signal is provided when the exhaust back pressure, from the cylinder, falls to zero. When pressure is exerted on the small poppet valve the main output line is closed (blocked).

Note: The graphic shown here shows the exhausting air at the cylinder port for ease of explanation. However, tubing takes the exhaust away via the directional control valve in the circuit.

Air jet sensing is also used to sense the position of a component or the presence of an object.

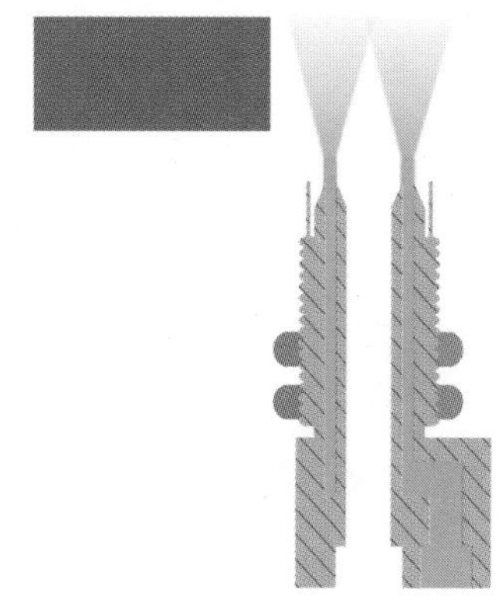

Low pressure air escapes from the jet nozzle to atmosphere. This is normally between 100 - 300 milli bar (1.45 - 4.35 psi or 10 Kpa - 30 Kpa).

When an object interrupts this flow of air, back pressure is created. This back pressure, usually between 0.5 and 3 milli bar (0.00725 - 0.0435 psi, or 50 - 300 pascals) is transmitted down the signal line which is then amplified and used to operate the next sequence.

Logic Valves

Logic valves, or elements as they are sometimes known, are miniature pneumatic valves.

The most common are the 'OR' valve and 'AND' valve.

'OR' Function

The 'OR' valve gives an output signal S when there is an input at 'a' or 'b' or both.

The equivalent valve in standard pneumatic components is the shuttle valve.

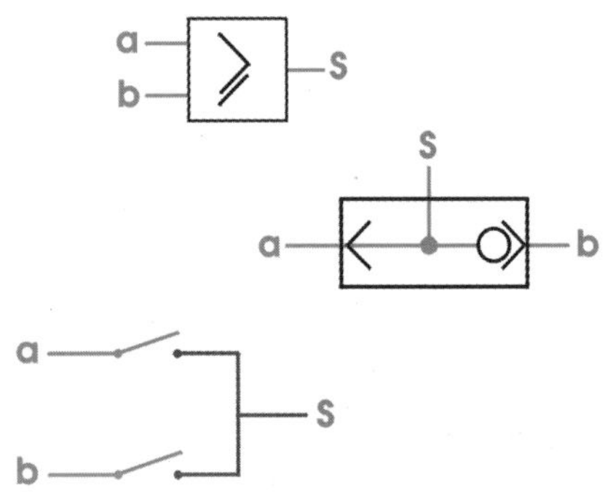

Here we see the symbol for the 'OR' valve and compare it with the equivalent pneumatic symbol and electrical symbol.

When an input is present at 'a' the poppet or shuttle moves over and gives an output signal at S.

Conversely if an input is present at 'b' we get an output signal S. This is also true if both inputs (a & b) are present.

If the inputs are of differing pressures say 3 bar (43.5 psi) and 5 bar (72.5 psi) the highest pressure will be the output signal. This is due to the higher pressure pushing the poppet or shuttle over.

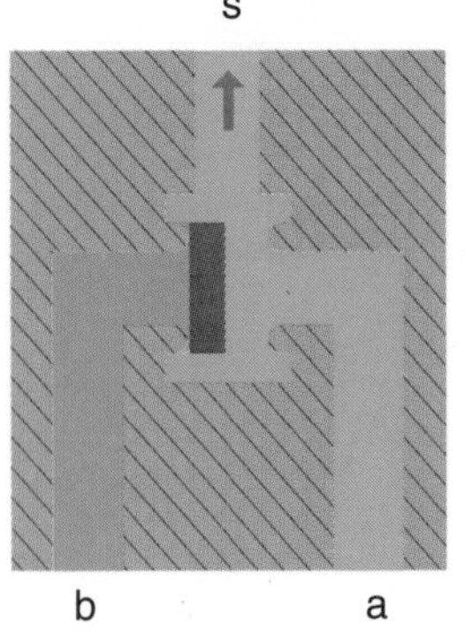

	a	b	s
1	0	0	0
2	0	1	1
3	1	0	1
4	1	1	1

Here is the **truth** table for the 'OR' valve. A 'Truth Table' shows the output status 'S' dependent on inputs 'a' and 'b' shown as logic '1' or logic '0'.

An off signal is shown as a Logic "0". An on signal is shown as a Logic "1". In line 1 we have 3 Logic "0"'s - no outputs. Line 2 shows a = "0", b = "1" therefore S = "1", Line 3 shows a = "1", b = "0" therefore S = "1". Line 4 shows a = "1", b = "1" therefore S = "1".

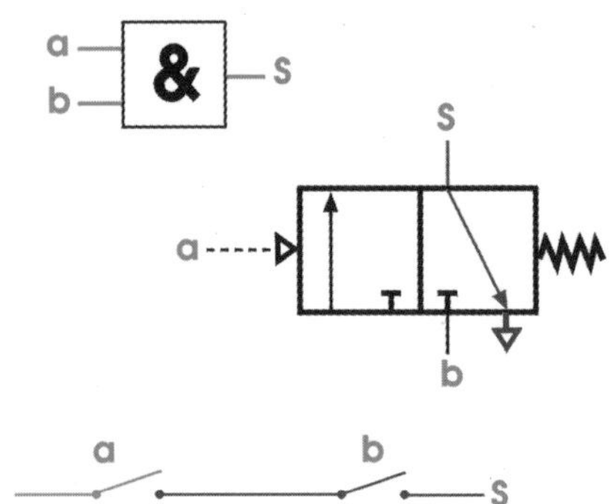

'And' Function

The 'AND' valve is also used regularly in logic circuitry.

Here we see the 'AND' symbol and compare it with the equivalent pneumatic valve and electrical symbols.

When an input is present at 'a' the poppet assembly moves over.

Only if both 'a' and 'b' are present is an output signal available.

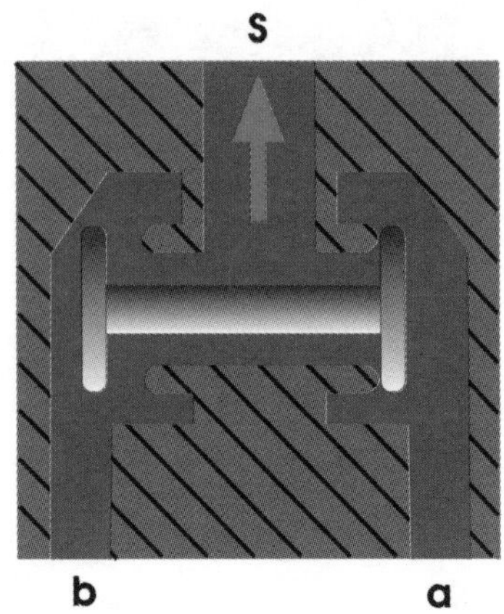

If the input signals are of differing pressures, say 3 bar (43.5 psi) and 5 bar (72.5 psi) the lowest pressure is the output signal S.

This is due to the higher pressure closing (blocking) the internal line and opening the lower pressure line.

This is due to Pascal's Law. Force = Area x Pressure.

Here we see the truth table for the 'AND' valve.

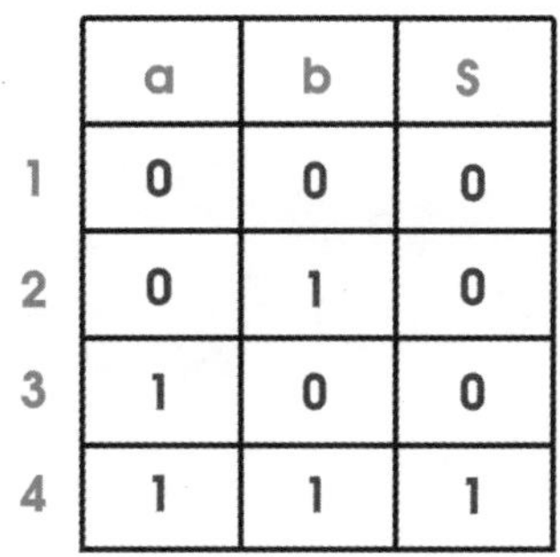

	a	b	S
1	0	0	0
2	0	1	0
3	1	0	0
4	1	1	1

Line 1 shows no inputs, therefore there are no outputs. Lines 2 and 3 show alternative inputs from 'a' and 'b' but there is no output. Only when there is a logic "1" at 'a' and a logic "1" at 'b' an output is achieved as shown in line 4.

'NOT' Inhibition Function

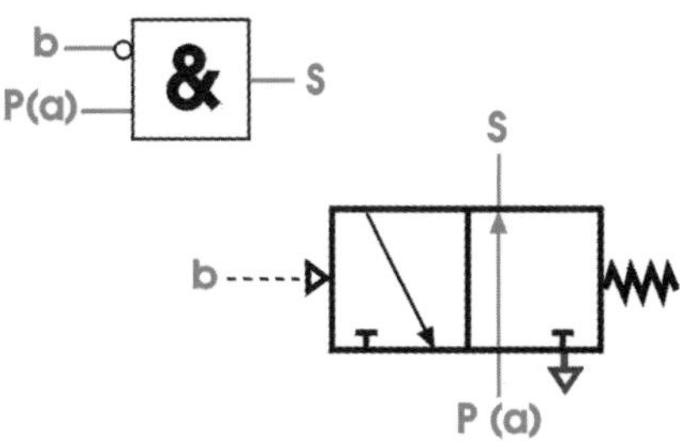

The 'NOT' valve is also a useful logic valve. This allows an output signal to be available until an input signal is present.

Here we see the 'NOT' (exclusion) symbol and compare it with the equivalent pneumatic symbol. 'a' could be a constant input 'p' of compressed air, or taken from some other part of the logic circuit depending on the design requirements.

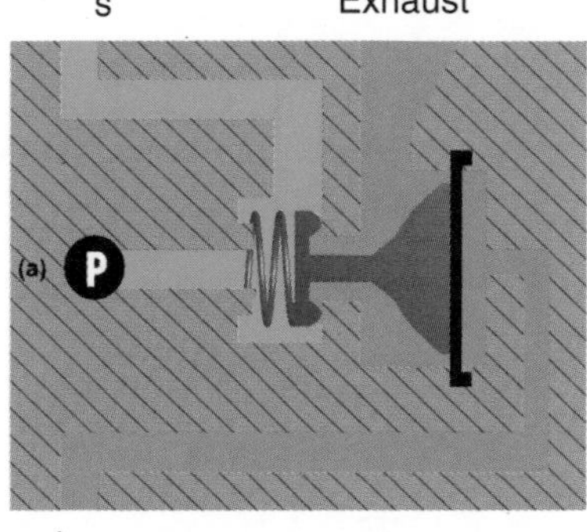

If 'a' is not a constant input this is called **inhibition**. In the neutral position air passes from 'a' (shown as a constant 'p') to 'S'. When a signal is received on port 'b', 'p' (a) is blocked and 'S' exhausts.

Line 1 of the truth table shows that with no input at 'a' or 'b' there is no output.

	a	b	S
1	0	0	0
2	0	1	0
3	1	0	1
4	1	1	0

Line 2 shows a Logic "0" at 'a' and a Logic "1" at 'b' with the result of still no output at "S".

If a Logic "1" is present 'a' and a Logic "0" at 'b' as shown in at line 3 of the truth table, an output, Logic "1" is present at "S". This would also be the case if 'a' had a constant signal which would be 'p'.

Line 4 in the truth table shows that if both 'a' and 'b' are present, output "S" is a Logic "0".

'YES' Function

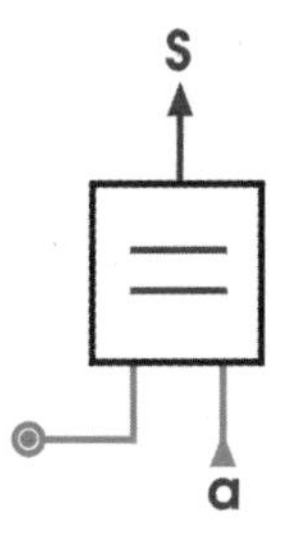

The yes or amplifier valve is used in conjunction with the normal 3 - 6 bar (42.5 - 87 psi) pneumatic valves where the input signal is only a few millibars of pressure.

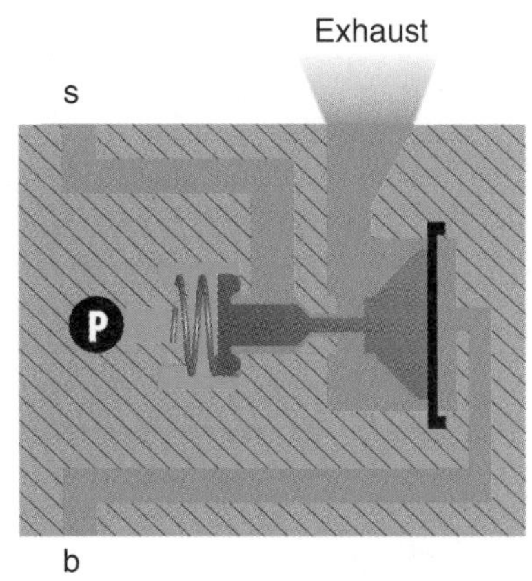

In the graphic main air pressure is available at 'p' which is in a closed (non-passing) position.

When a very low pressure signal is applied to the large diaphragm the valve operates and gives a main air output to operate the next sequence within the circuit.

The 'jet sensor' has been described previously and here the amplifier is shown in the circuit.

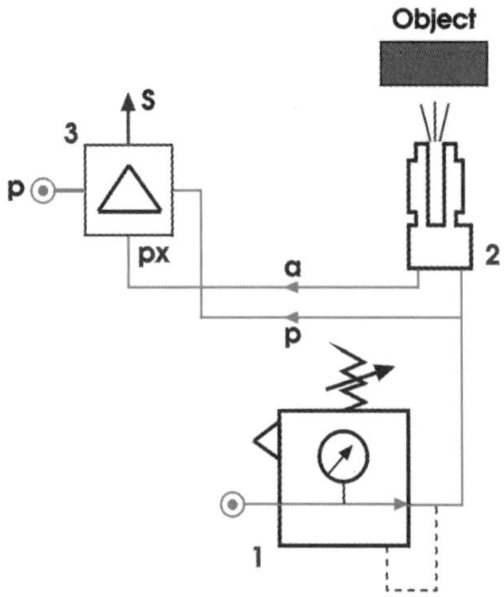

Valve 1 is a low pressure regulator which reduces the pressure to between 100 - 300 milli bar (1.45 - 4.35 psi). This pressure operates the jet sensor '2' and the amplifier '3' at port "Px". The amplifier has a permanent 3 - 6 bar (42.5 - 87 psi) pressure input connected to it at "P".

When an object is sensed at the jet nozzle, a back pressure of 0.5 - 3 milli bar (0.00725 -0.0435 psi) is generated down signal line 'a'.

The amplifier operates and gives an output at signal "S".

Bleed Sensor / Relay

The bleed sensor relay is designed to feed a bleed sensor and to generate a pneumatic signal in reaction to the blocking of the sensor.

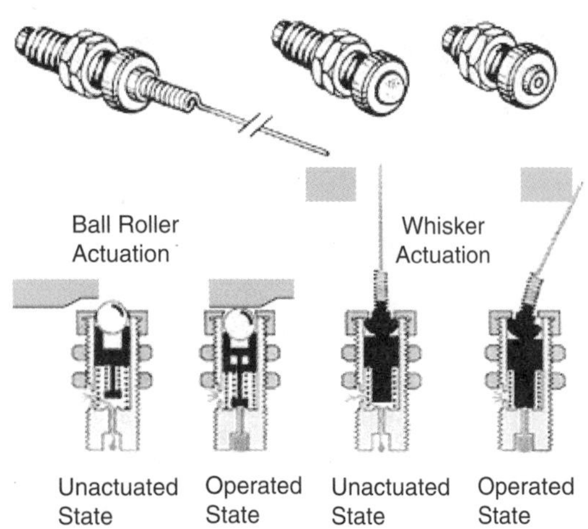

Bleed sensors can be direct action, ball roller action or whisker action.

They require only one tube connection, have small actuating forces, short travel and are very compact.

In the unactuated state air is supplied to the bleed sensor through a filter and fixed orifice of 0.3 mm (0.12") diameter.

Looking at the diagram on the opposite page the resulting bleed 'a' is virtually inaudible and consumption is negligible.

The main pressure is supplied at 'p' and the output port is 'S'.

When the bleed sensor is blocked the pressure rises in the connection tube linking the relay to the sensor.

This pressure switches the relay by acting on the pilot diaphragm.

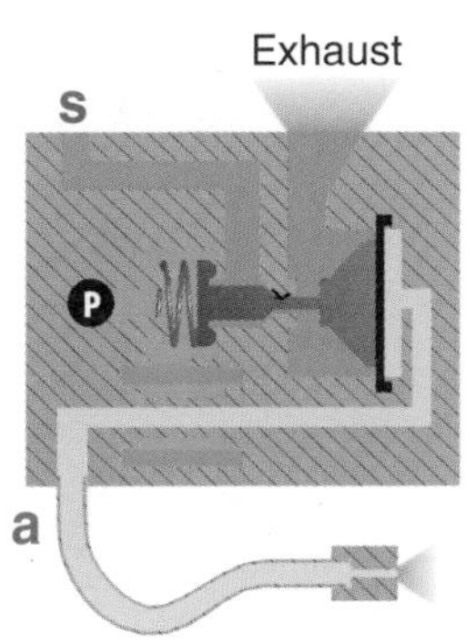

The poppet assembly shifts allowing air to pass from 'p' to 'S'.

Timers

Logic timers can be either positive output or negative output.

With the positive timer, when an input signal at 'a' is applied, an adjustable time delay occurs.

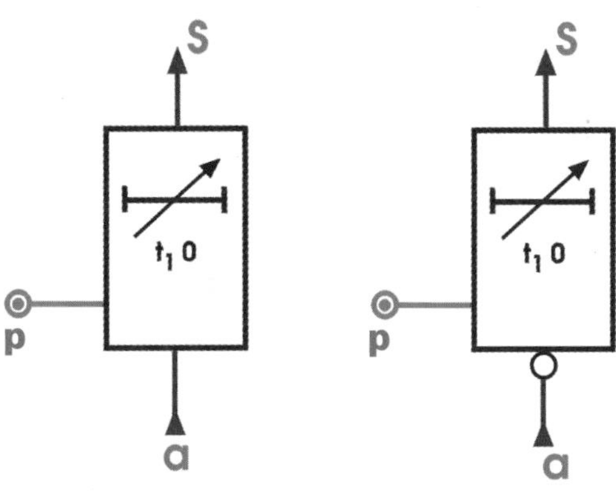

After the time delay is complete, an output signal appears at "S".

With the negative timer, when the air supply "P" is present, an output "S" is also present.

When the input signal 'a' is applied, a time delay occurs. When this is complete the output signal is switched off.

Memory Function

The pneumatic switching memory function changes state from '0', (non passing) to '1', (passing) when it receives a signal from 'a' or 'b'. Main pressure is available at 'p'. Here is the logic symbol for the memory function with the equivalent pneumatic symbol. The valves are bi-stable and only change state when a signal is placed on 'a' or 'b'.

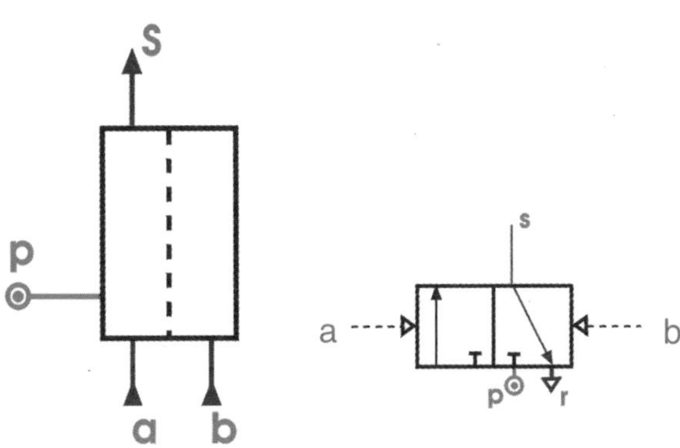

To get an output, a signal is received at 'a' operating the pilot diaphragm which opens the poppet assembly.

Output is achieved at "S".

If the signal is removed from 'a' the valve will remain in this last position.

Note that the indicator is also operated showing that an output is present.

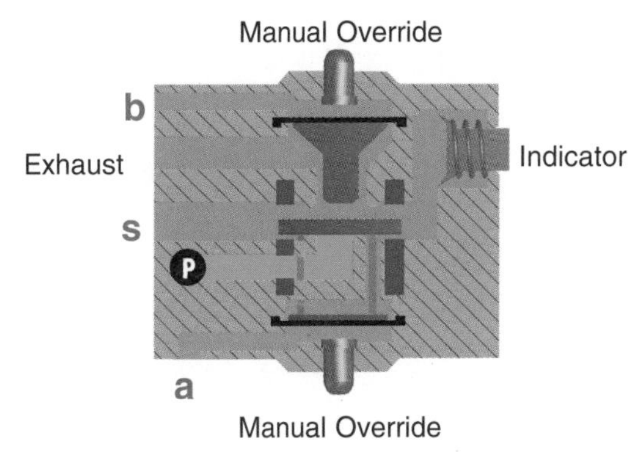

To reset the valve and to exhaust and switch off the output at "S" a signal is given at port 'b'.

The diaphragm and plunger are operated resetting the poppet assembly.

The indicator also resets showing that no output is present.

Push buttons are on each side of the valve to enable manual setting or resetting of the memory valve. This is the manual override.

Sequential Control

Introduction

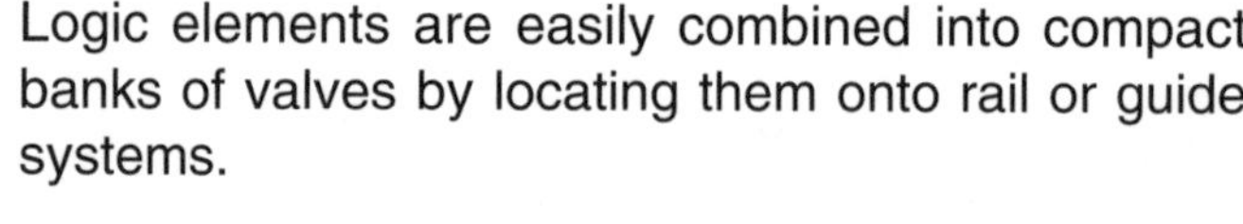

Logic elements are easily combined into compact banks of valves by locating them onto rail or guide systems.

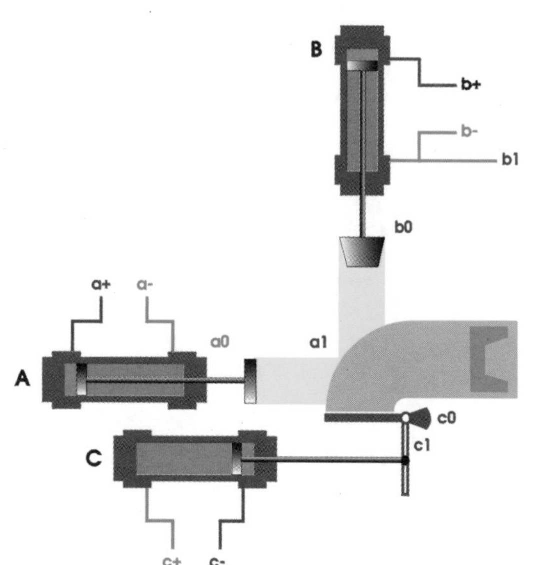

They can also be incorporated with sequencer step modules to produce a quick easy control circuit.

Here we see a typical pneumatic machine application.

Cylinder "A" transfers a component. Cylinder "B" forms the component.

Cylinder "C" ejects the component. Note that this cylinder is extended in the start position. "cO" is operated as this is the cylinder's start position.

All cylinders are operated by 5/2 directional control valves (which are not shown for ease of clarity); these valves are pilot operated, and therefore cylinder movement is represented by the lines shown going into the cylinder and designated: a+, a-, b+, b-, c+, c-.

The end of stroke feedback signals are provided by position sensors or mechanical limit switches or as by 'b1' a pressure threshold detector.

A manual push button (m) starts the cycle.

The sequence is start (m)

A+
B+, A-
B-
C-
C+
Stop / Repeat

Five steps in all require a five module sequencer, one sequencer module per step. Instant tubing connections are made to each step module.

Grafcet

Sequential control can easily be done utilizing the Grafcet System.

Grafcet is a function diagram configuration which defines the operating cycle. Fig 1.

A sequencer stage module corresponds to each stage in the cycle.

The actuated stage module sends the control signal to the pressure valve controlling the action intended for the stage.

It then waits for the feedback signal at the end of this action before actuating the next stage module in the sequencer.

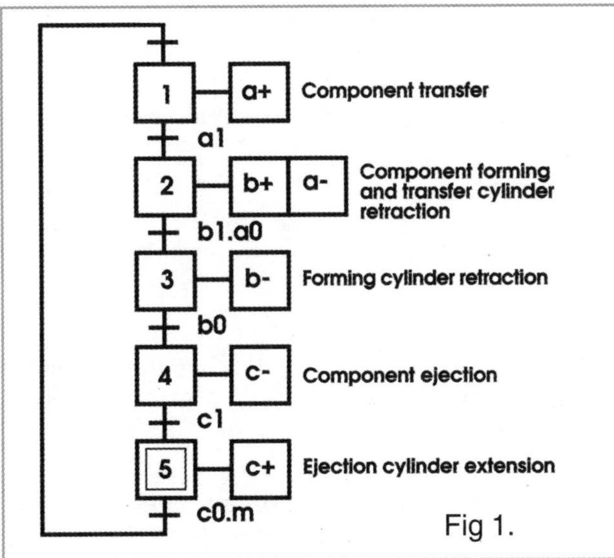

Fig 1.

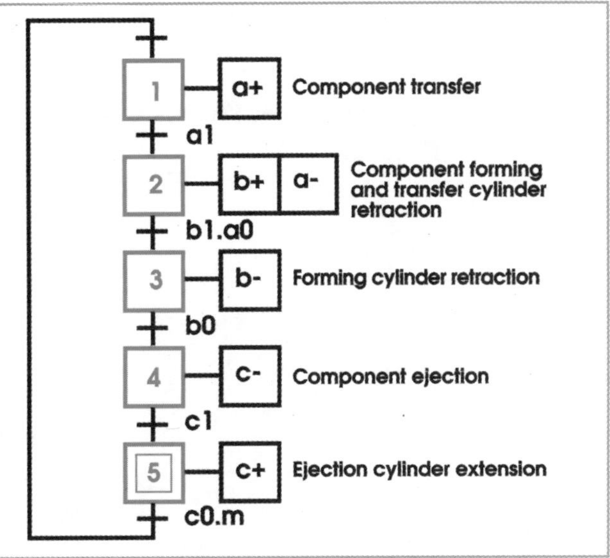

The operating cycle is shown here. Each operation is shown in box form. In this case 1 to 5 Fig 2.

Cylinder movement is shown in another box attached to the sequence box. Fig 3.

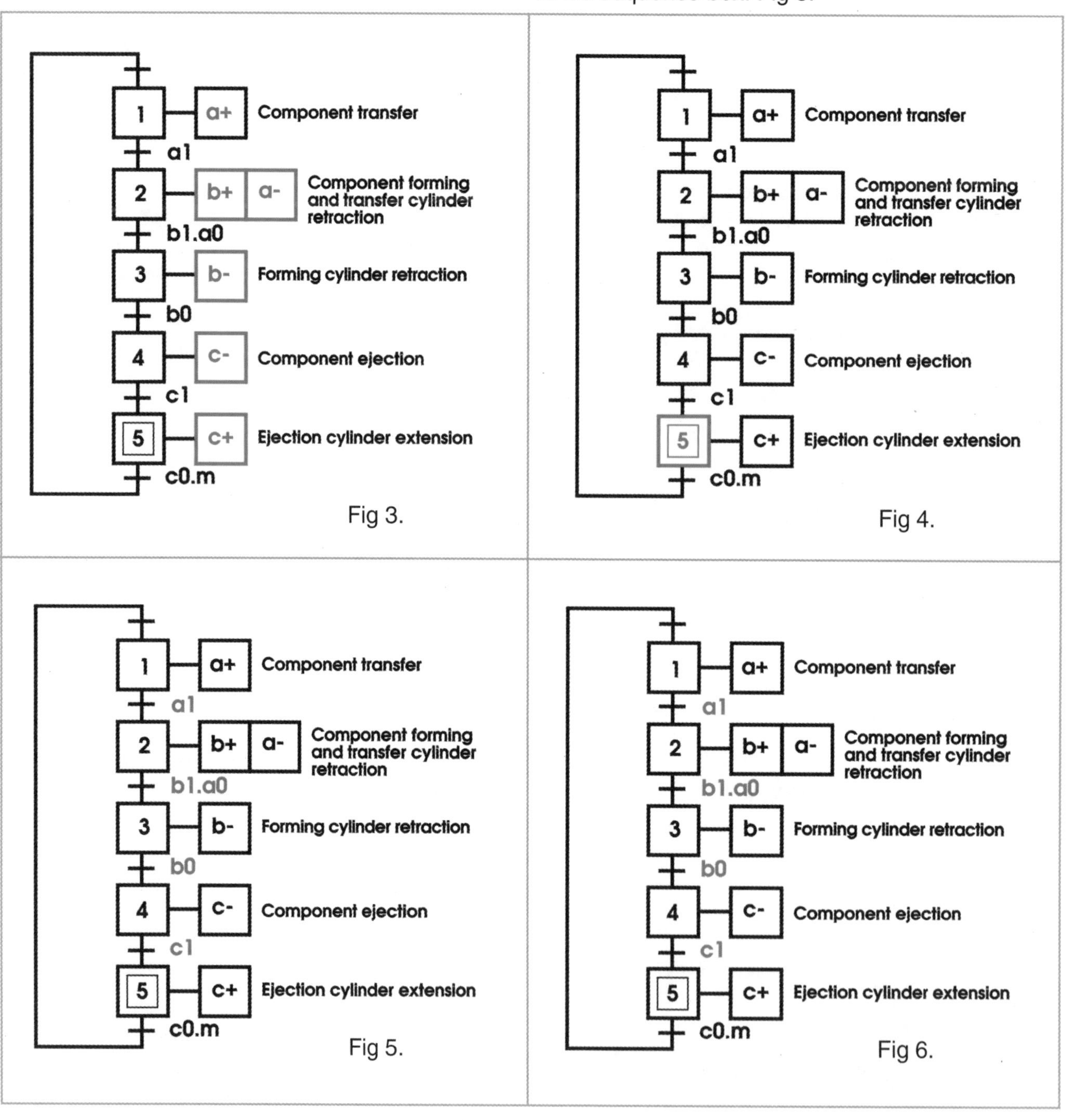

Fig 3.

Fig 4.

Fig 5.

Fig 6.

Therefore each stage is recorded. Note that at Stage 2 cylinder 'b' extends while cylinder 'a' retracts. This is classed as one sequential stage.

The final stage 5 has two squares, one inside the other, to identify the last operation before the cycle starts again. Fig 4.

Between each stage the corresponding signal is shown. Fig 5. This must be made before the cycle can continue.

After stage 5 switch 'Co' must be made and the start button 'm' operated before the cycle can continue. Fig 6.

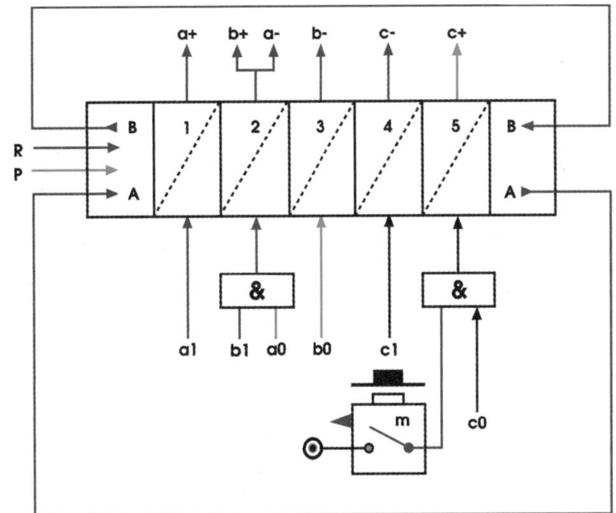

Basic Sequential Operation

The sequence has 5 modules marked 1 - 5. Main air is supplied to the modules via 'P' and the modules exhaust via 'R'.

Port A of the last module is connected to port A of the first module via the 'Tail' and 'Head' modules.

When a signal is present, this starts the cycle.

Port B of the head and tail modules are also connected together to give a feedback signal. This signal resets the last module.

Each sequence module, when operated by an input signal, resets the previous sequence module output and sets the next output.

This eliminates all possibility of trapped signals on the pilot actuators of the 5/2 directional control valves.

Operation of Sequential Circuit

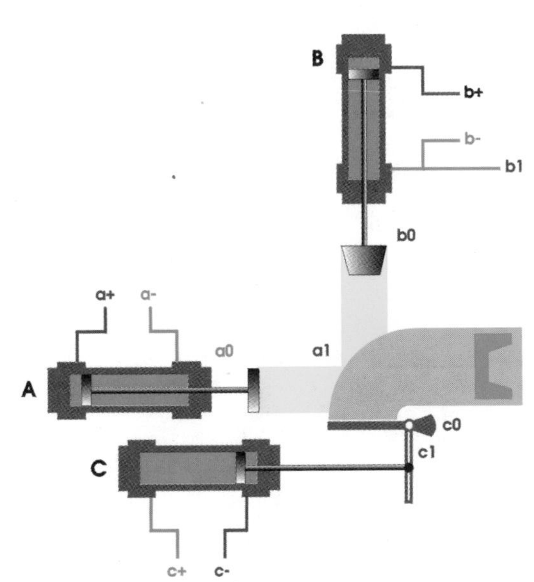

When the start button (m) is operated this completes the 'AND' function with 'c0'. An output is given by module 1 and cylinder A extends (A+). Note that the signals to the directional control valves are shown as a+, b+, a-, b-, c- and c+. These operate the pilot actuators of the valves.

Signal valve 'a1', is operated (made). This resets Module 1 and sets Module 2. The output of Module 2 extends cylinder B and retracts cylinder A (B+A-).

When cylinder B is fully extended (b1) and cylinder A fully retracted (a0) the 'AND' function is made and Module 2 is reset Module 3 gives an output which retracts cylinder B (B-).

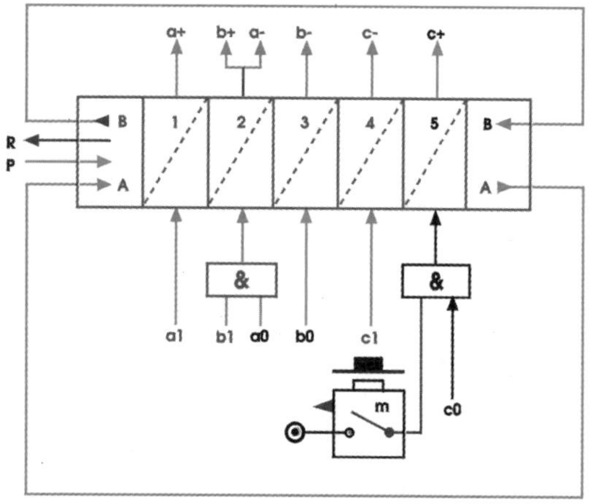

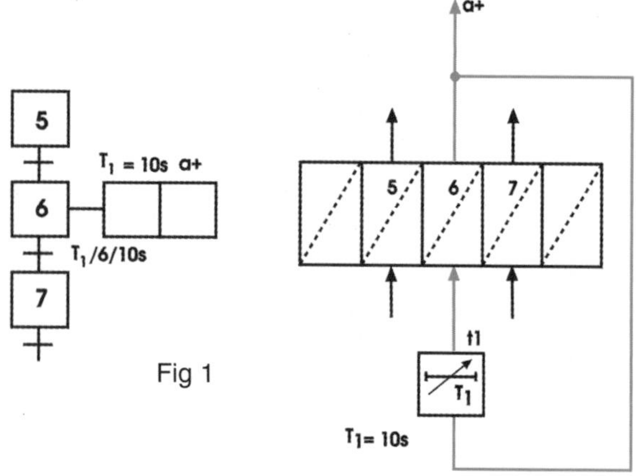

Fig 1

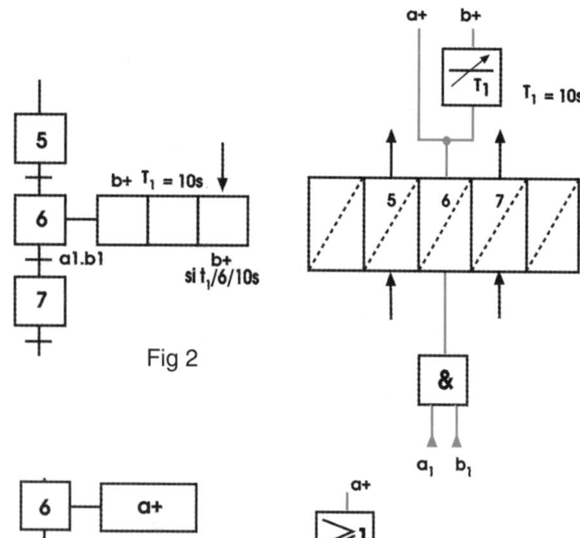

Fig 2

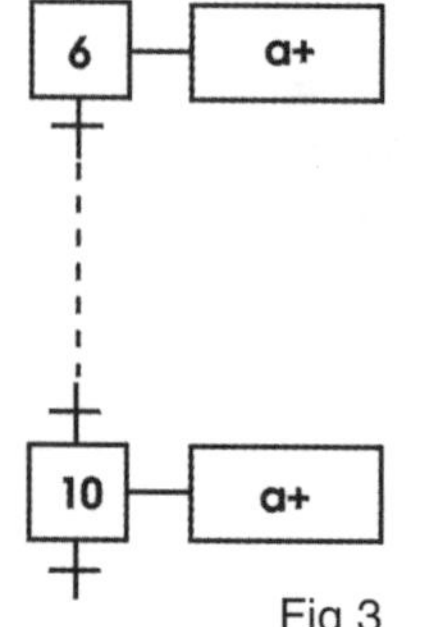

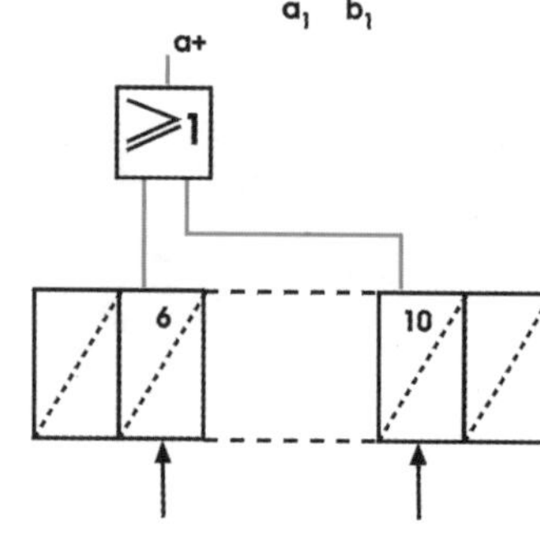

Fig 3

Signal valve 'b0' is then actuated (made), resetting Module 3 and setting the output on Module 4. Cylinder C retracts (C-).
On full retraction valve 'c1' is operated resetting Module 4 and setting Module 5. Cylinder C extends (C+).

The cycle is now complete and 'c0' is operated (made) on full extension of cylinder C, its rest position.

If start valve 'm' was of the detent lever type, and was actuated, this would give a continual cycle.

Two 'AND' functions are incorporated into the circuit; one ensures that 'b1' and 'a0' are both operated before the next sequence, B-, takes place. This also applies to the start 'm' and 'c0'.

Manual overide buttons are incorporated into the sequence modules to enable the sequence to be operated manually.

They also have visual indicators to show which step module has an output. This aids fault finding.

Time delays can be also incorporated into the sequencer.

Here is a 'Time Delay Action' Grafcet together with the sequencer circuit, Fig 1.

The output of Module 6 is connected to a timer module back to the input of Module 6 to give a time delay of 10 seconds before Module 7 operates.

Here is a 'Delayed Action' Grafcet and sequencer circuit, Fig 2.

The output of Module 6 gives a time delay of 10 seconds before b+ operates and both 'a1' and 'b1' must be made before the sequence continues.

And finally here is a 'Repetitive Action' Grafcet and the sequence circuit. Both sequences Modules 6 and

10 extend cylinder "A" therefore and 'OR' valve is placed between both output lines. Fig 3.

Summary

Logic uses small pneumatic valves to give various functions.

They are used in various industries including munitions, the gas industry and where compact automation systems are required.

Signal valves are miniature in construction.

Position sensors have mechanical or non contact actuation including jet sensing and end of stroke pressure sensing.

Logic elements are rail mounted and include OR, AND, NOT and YES functions.

Sequential control using the Grafcet function diagram is easily achieved.

Sequence stage modules supply output signals to pneumatic control valves to produce the required sequence.

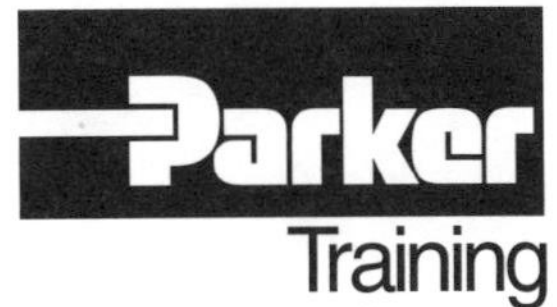

Module 7

Maintenance and Fault Finding

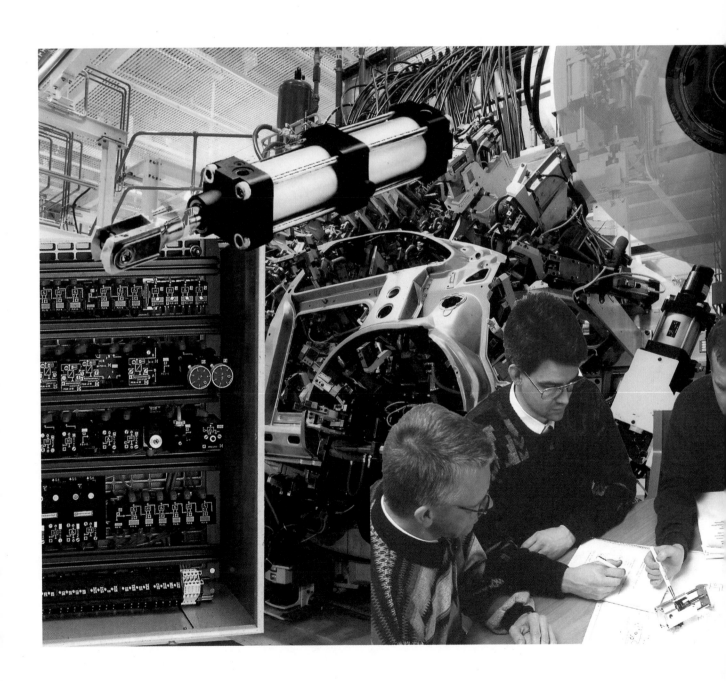

Contents

Introduction

Maintenance of pneumatic equipment is very important to ensure the safe and efficient use of the compressed air in the system and its components.

Prevention is always better than cure and is generally less expensive in the long term.

Contamination in the form of water and dust particles cause up to 70% of the failures in compressed air systems.

It is therefore imperative to include and maintain such items as:

- aftercoolers
- dryers
- filters
- lubricators

However machines and equipment do fail from time to time and must be repaired or replaced.

Fault finding must be done in a logical manner using circuit diagrams and manufacturer's data whenever possible.

This logical approach is always quicker and takes into account all safety aspects relative to compressed air.

Objectives

In this module we will be looking at:

- Maintenance requirements
- Good maintenance practice
- Leak detection
- Fault finding / trouble shooting techniques
- Equipment faults

Maintenance

What is good maintenance?

Good maintenance is:

- Using common sense
- Stop - do not attempt to remove any item or component from a pressurized system
- Look - for any damaged equipment and check pressures are correct
- Listen - for any leaks or undue noise coming from the compressed air system

Before attempting to maintain any equipment.

Remember good working practices and all safety aspects before removing any item from a system.

Depressurize the system fully and use lock out valves as required by codes and standards.

Keep all tools and replacement parts clean. Use only manufacturer's recommended spares.

Change compressor oils according to the manufacturer's time schedules and maintain filters, regulators and lubricators regularly.

Always maintain up-to-date records.

The **'good guys'** are:

Cleanliness
High quality oils and materials
Proper filters
Good seals
Normal operation at the correct
Pressures, flow and temperatures

The **'bad guys'** are:

Moisture
Dirt
Heat
Abuse

Leaks

Although compressed air leaks do not create a house-keeping problem like a hydraulic leak, fixing them is important.

There is not only a safety risk of serious injury from an air leak entering the blood stream but leaks waste compressed air and reduce machine and component performance.

Leaks may drastically reduce efficiency by lowering both the pressure and air flow available.

It is therefore obvious that leaks are kept to a minimum by checking the system regularly.

Serious leaks are audible and can be heard normally at the end of the day or at a weekend when machines are turned off.

Tests can be done with soapy water to check for a leak - **never** use fingers or hands to detect leaks.

There are aerosols available which can be sprayed onto suspect fittings and very sophisticated ultrasonic leak detectors are also available.

Pipe runs can be checked for leaks by pressurizing the system to a given pressure.

Isolate the section and note how long it takes for the pressure to drop to a minimum value.

This can be done at night or during the weekend when the systems can be isolated and it allows sufficient time to complete any repairs. Leaks with the equivalent of a 13mm (1/2") hole will release to atmosphere approximately 34,000 cubic metres (1.2 million cubic feet) of air per month.

This is equivalent to $1,200 or £800 per month of electrical cost of compressing the air and keeping the compressor running to make up the losses.

A 10% drop in air pressure due to leaks reduces the efficiency of an air tool by as much as 15%.

Fault Finding / Trouble Shooting

Good trouble shooting is:-

1 Gathering of **preliminary information**

2 Carrying out of **preliminary checks**

3 Fault / failure diagnosis

4 Testing of suspected components

Preliminary Information

Helps to decide the basic failure. The best source of this information is the operator of the faulty machine or plant.

Preliminary information to be gathered:-

1. Under what conditions does or did the failure occur?

   a. Does it occur on one actuator or on all actuators?
   b. Does it occur in one direction or both directions?
   c. Does it occur under light or heavy loading, or both?

2. Type of failure (how does failure show itself)?

   a. Complete failure of motion or motions?
   b. Sluggish reactions?

3. Failure occurrence (how often) ?

   a. Did the failure occur suddenly or develop gradually?
   b. Is it a periodic failure?

4. System Interface i.e.

Has any unauthorized person been carrying out adjustments? If so, what adjustments?

Has anyone (including the operator) attempted to cure the failure? If so, what steps did they carry out?

Preliminary Checks

1) Check if compressed air is available at the correct pressure.

2) Are compressors / motors running and are they running noisy and / or hot?

3) Are filters clean?

4) Check pressure conditions under all motions and when actuators are stationary.

Failure Diagnosis (Determination of possible causes)

Failure diagnosis must be carried out while consulting the circuit diagram logically, "**Area by Area**", component by component and assessing the likelihood of any particular component of causing the problem.

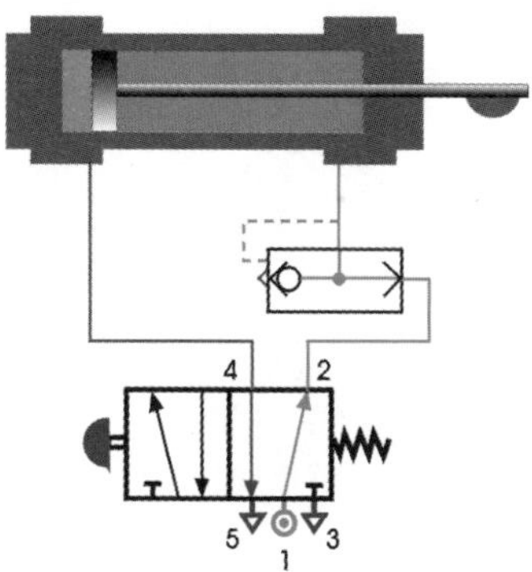

From the preliminary information obtained, it should be possible to determine in which area of the circuit the problem lies.

For example, in a simple circuit, the area to be considered would be the complete circuit, the preliminary information gained must be used to locate the area in which the failure or problem lies.

When the possible causes of trouble have been determined **then and only then** should actual tests be carried out on suspected components.

Note that also included in a circuit are stop valves, filters, regulators and lubricators which should also be included in failure diagnosis.

Testing of Suspected Components

When testing a suspected component, the actual failures which might occur in it, giving faulty performance and hence a failure in the system, should be kept in mind.

1) Carry out easiest checks on suspected components; e.g., check manually operated lever movements.

Mr. Hit or Miss

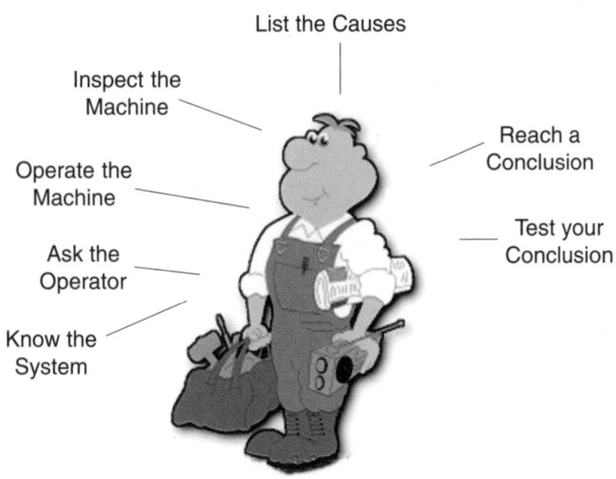

Mr. Trouble Shooter

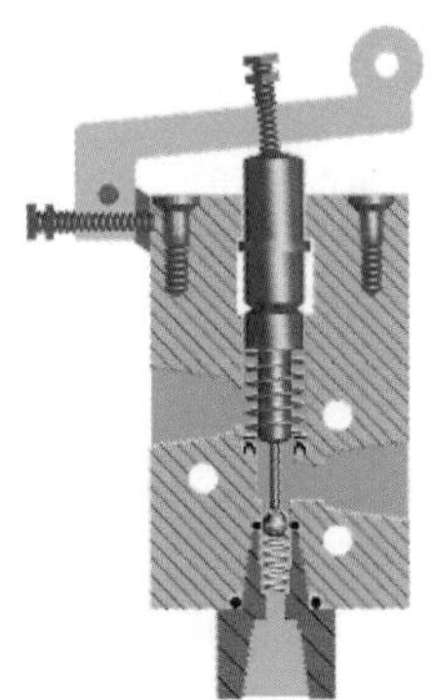

Manually check solenoid operated valves by operating the manual override. Ensure that actuators **do not** create a danger if the valve operates. Check the pressure regulator valve for proper and correct adjustment.

2) Select the item **most likely** to be causing the fault and check it first, then work through the others progressively.

3) If a suspected item is relatively easy to check, this should be checked before more difficult items.

4) Test suspected items in position in the circuit if possible. Always remember '**Safety first**'.

Don't be a 'hit or miss' guy or 'trial and error' parts replacer.

Working logically and methodically will produce quicker results and be cost effective.

Equipment Faults / Failures

Valves

Valves may have to be removed from the system for maintenance. This should be done at a 'shutdown' period. To achieve full efficiency and service from valves, uncontaminated air should be used.

Poppet Valves

Poppet valves, because of their construction, generally have a long working life.

The flow of air travelling over the poppet cleans the mechanism each time it is operated.

However, if the air is contaminated with water or small dirt particles this will shorten the life span of this or any valve.

Seals subjected to this abrasion will wear and eventually leak air either to the atmosphere through the exhaust port, or into the system, which could inadvertently operate another valve or actuator.

Spool Valves

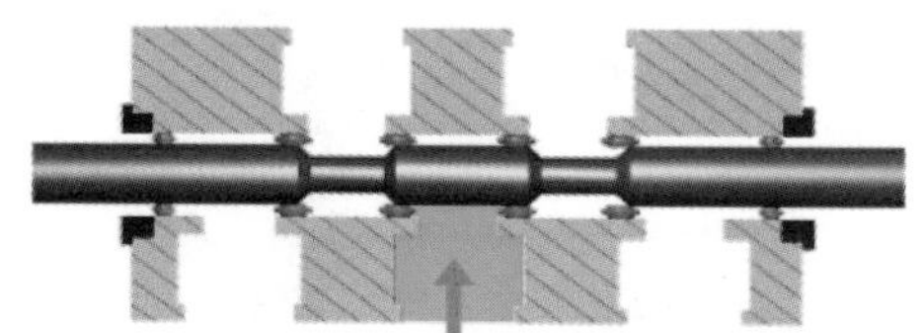

Spool valves require regular maintenance as do all pneumatic valves and components to ensure high operational efficiency.

Although 'O' rings are specifically compounded for wear and abrasion resistance they must be inspected regularly.

Look for wear and flexibility of the seals.

Inspect the seals for leakage.

Check the lands of the spool for scoring which indicates that the air is contaminated with abrasive material or moisture.

Inspect the edges of the spool for burring. If the valve is of the static 'O' ring type then these burrs will cut and damage the 'O' rings.

If there is a spring in the valve, ensure that it is not blocked down the center with the packed dirt.

The spool will not be able to move its full travel under this condition.

'O' Ring Failures

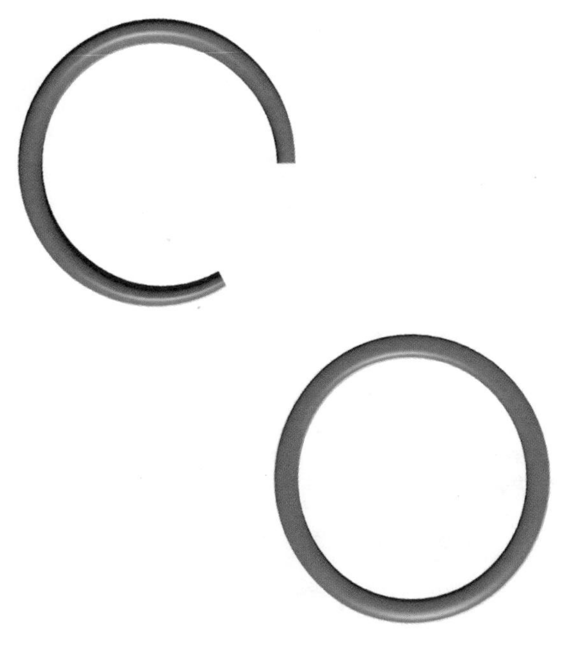

Here we see the most common causes of 'O' ring failure.

Always use seals which are recommended by the manufacturers of the equipment. Using cheaper seals is not always profitable. A broken 'O' ring serves no purpose and could create a safety situation by allowing air to pressurize the circuit, and permitting a load to move or just loss of air.

A worn 'O' ring generally means that there has been little or no lubrication and friction has caused it to wear. If the 'O' ring is flattened or worn then low grade or non-standard seals have been used or they were pinched at assembly.

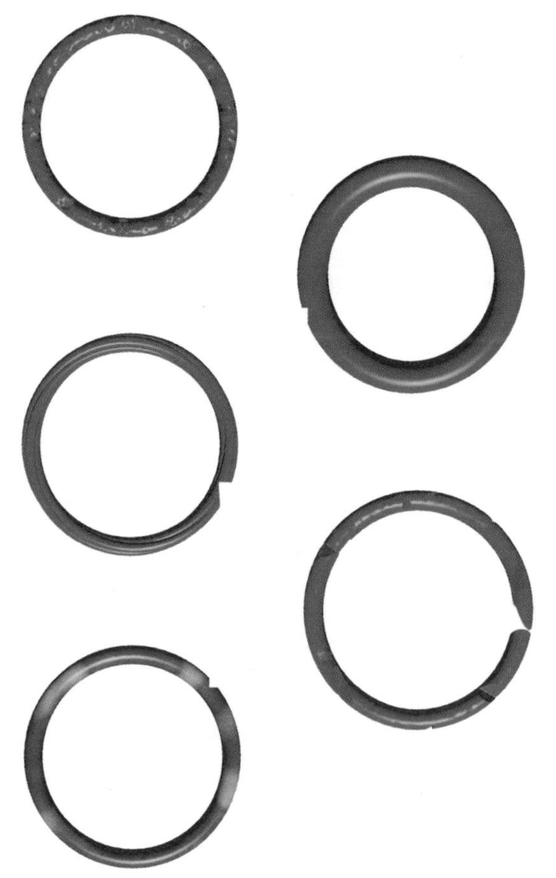

Cracked 'O' rings have normally been subjected to too much heat or conversely by severe cold. If the equipment is working in a hot environment seals made from material such as Viton should be used.

A swollen 'O' ring will create high friction and in some cases will stick moving parts. The 'O' ring has possibly been subjected to the wrong lubricant.

Always check with the supplier if the oil or grease is compatible with the 'O' ring material.

Twisted 'O' rings mean that the seal has been installed incorrectly and has rolled around itself or has been subjected to high friction or "backup" rings are missing. If this happens regularly check the installation procedures.

A cut 'O' ring again may have been installed incorrectly or subjected to burrs or damaged spools, shafts or grooves.

Finally dirty 'O' rings have probably had poor storage, being subjected to system contamination, or installed in an unclean environment.

Cleanliness is of paramount importance when installing or maintaining compressed air system components.

Therefore always keep the maintenance area clean.

Barrel/Tube
Head/Front End Cap
'O' Ring
Cap/Rear End Cap
Cushion Seal
Piston Rod
Wiper/Scraper Seal
Pressure Seal
Piston
Piston Seal

Scored Bearing Rod Gland/Rod Bearing
Damaged Scraper Ring
Scored Piston

Cylinder failures

Pneumatic cylinders are very efficient and have a long working life if the air supplied to them is uncontaminated.

They are also subjected to high forces and stresses due to the pull and push loading during their working cycle. This can result in cylinder failure over a period of time.

If the piston rod is exposed to external contamination this can score the rod.

This in turn can damage the wiper seal and rod seal resulting in air leaks. Further wear can damage the rod gland allowing unacceptable lateral piston rod movement.

Contaminated air will drastically reduce the life of a pneumatic cylinder.

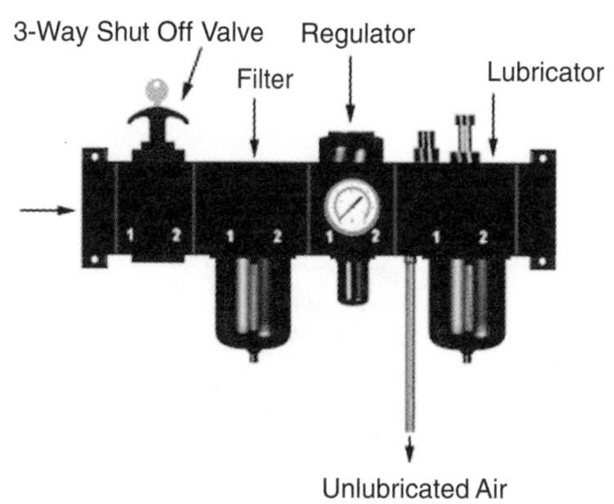

Lubricants can be 'washed' from the seals and barrel by wet, contaminated air which result in high wear rate.
In non-lubricated air systems dry, clean air must be supplied to the cylinder or the permanent lubrication may be lost. In lubricated systems clean oil of the recommended type must be used.

It is advisable in all cylinder circuits to use filters and lubricators.

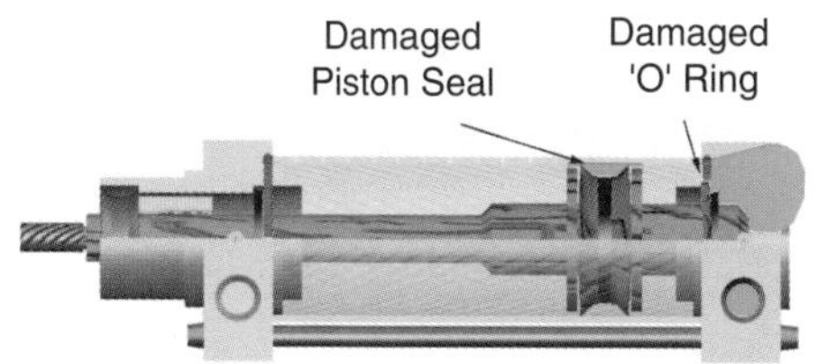

Abrasive contaminants will damage the piston seals which will result in leakage between the seal and the cylinder barrel. Air escaping through the cylinder's directional control valve exhaust port may be an indication of this. A damaged seal between the barrel and the cap will result in a loss of air.

FRLs - Filters

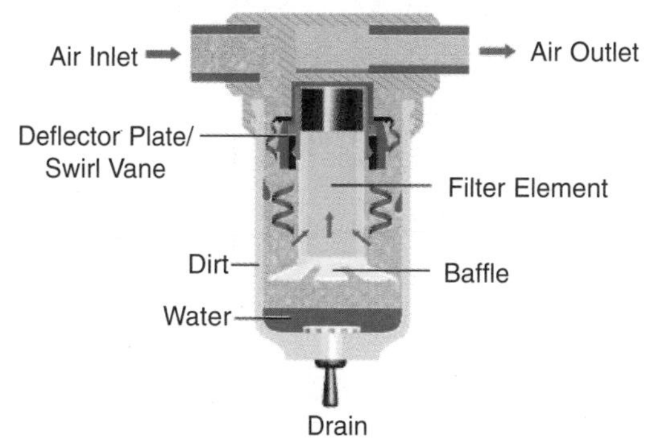

Filters, because of their role in a compressed air system, require more frequent maintenance than other components.

If they are not maintained the filter element or mechanism will choke or fill up with contamination.

A pressure drop will result and downstream pressure will be reduced as will the air flow.

The result of this will be loss of force or torque at an actuator and / or lack of speed.

Filters with polycarbonate bowls allow the contamination to be seen. Some metal bowls do not, so these must be checked regularly. **Only** the condensate level can be seen in the sight glass.

If a polycarbonate bowl requires cleaning only use soap and water or as directed by the manufacturer.

Never use solvents as these will attack the bowl and create a safety hazard. The bowl may fail..

Pressure Regulators

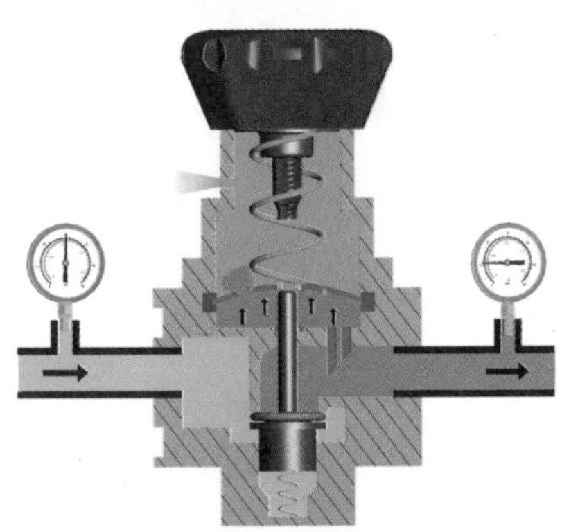

The life of a pressure regulator is high and therefore little maintenance is required. Always ensure that there is a filter preceding a pressure regulator to remove contamination

The problem faults that may occur in a pressure regulator are worn seals or a worn or damaged diaphragm.

On a self venting pressure regulator this can be detected as air escaping through the vent hole constantly.

Lubricators

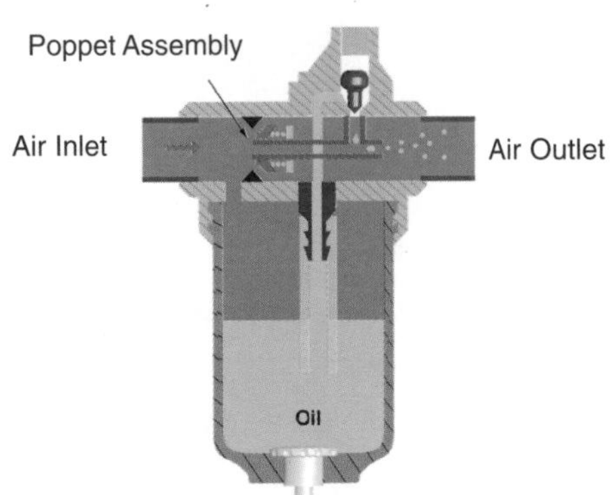

Lubricators are very efficient and if the correct type of oil is used and it is cleaned regularly then little additional maintenance will be required. It is however advisable to precede the lubricator with a filter to remove contamination.

As with any industrial component, maintenance is essential. The better the maintenance the less chance a problem will occur.

Always replace parts with the ones recommended by the manufacturer. These will give longer life and ensure maximum efficiency.

Summary

Before removing any suspected components from the circuit, the following points should be checked. All electrical supplies should be isolated or shut off - **safety first**.

- All compressors should be stopped or fully isolated, release pressure.
- Ensure that the component being removed will not release any residual pressure in the line, for example, due to supported loads.
- When dealing with items such as sub plate mounted valves. Ensure that 'O' rings are not lost.

- Keep personnel clear of actuators (e.g. if checking solenoid valves manually, this may actuate the actuators).
- When not sure about construction of a suspected component, consult service manual, to avoid damage, lost parts, personnel injury etc.
- Parts removed should be cleaned before replacement
- When dismantling a component, e.g. a valve, take care with any parts that have a spring behind them, both to prevent personal injury and loss of spring
- Replace worn or damaged items with ones recommended by the manufacturer
- When repairing a cylinder or valve change all the seals which are supplied in the repair kit, not just the damaged ones. This will ensure a longer life.
- Never clean a polycarbonate filter bowl with solvents, use soap and water only.
- Remember prevention is better than cure.

Module 8

Database and Glossary

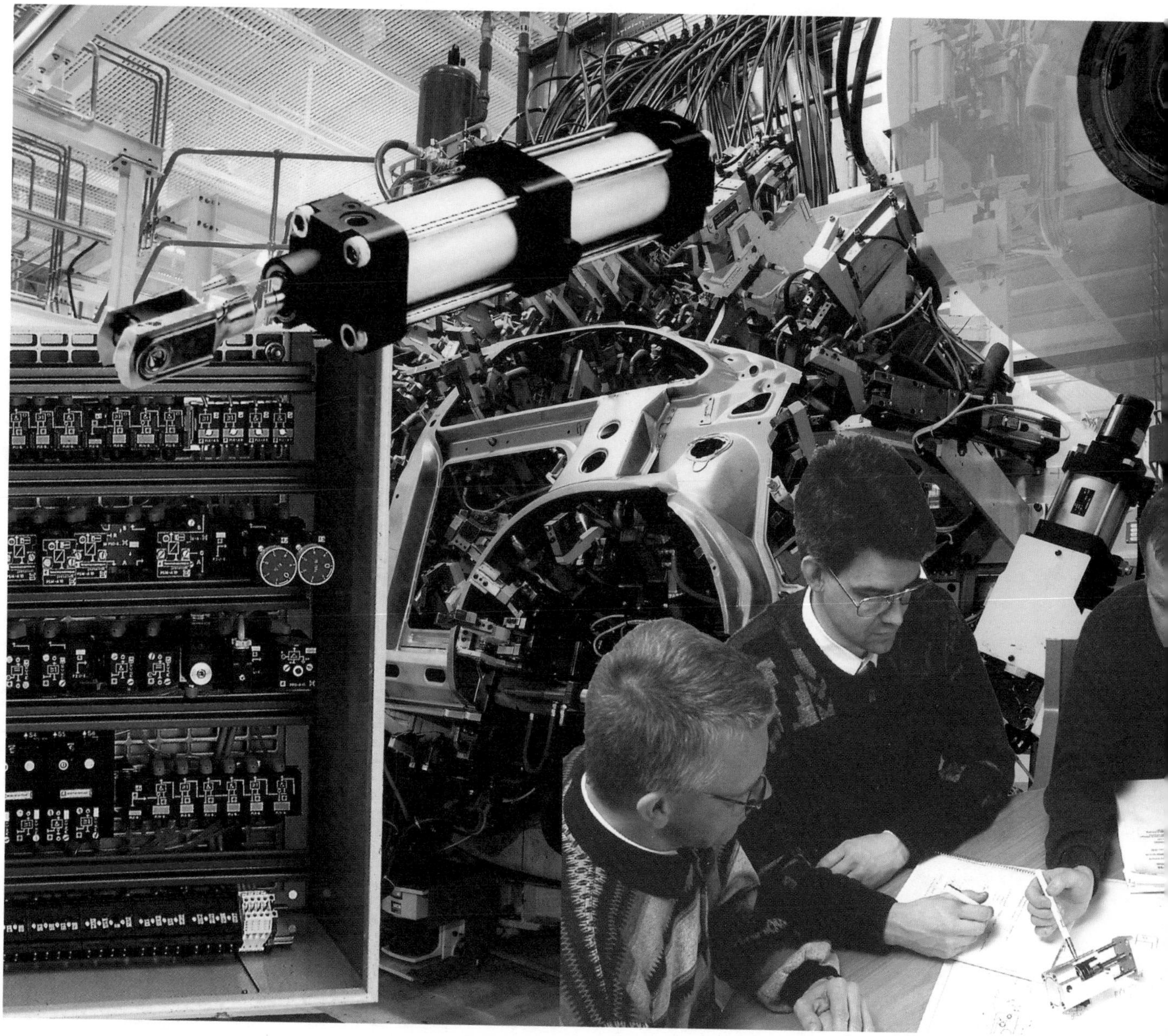

Database And Glossary

Gas Laws / Formulae

Pneumatic Principles

1. All gases are compressible

2. Compressed air has the property of 'elasticity', i.e. it exerts pressure on all surfaces of the vessel in which it is enclosed

3. Force = Push or pull exerted against an area

4. Force = Pressure x Area

5. Force x Distance = Work

6. Pascal's Law:

   "Pressure exerted on a confined gas is transmitted undiminished in all directions ...and with equal force on equal areas"

7. Boyle / Marriot's Law:

   $P_1 \times V_1 = C$

   "The pressure and volume of a particular quantity of gas is constant provided the temperature does not vary."

8. Charles's / Gay Lussac's Law:

   $$V_1 = V_2 \times \frac{T_1}{T_2}$$

   "At constant pressure the volume of a gas increases in proportion to the temperature."

Units of Measurement - Unit Names

Quantity	Name of Unit	Value	Symbol
Length	**Metre**	**Base Unit**	**m**
	centimetre	0.01m	cm
	millimetre	0.001m	mm
	micrometre	0.000001m	µm
	kilometre	1,000m	km
	international nautical mile (for navigation)	1,852m	n mile
Mass	**Kilogram**	**BaseUnit**	**Kg**
	milligram	0.000 001kg	mg
	gram	0.001kg	g
	tonne	1,000kg	t
Time	**Second**	**Base Unit**	**s**
	minute	60s	min
	hour	60 min	h
	day	24h	d
Area	**Square Metre**	**SI Unit**	**m sq**
	square millimetre	0.000 001m sq	mm sq
	square centimetre	0.000 1m sq	cm sq
	hectare	10,000 m sq	ha
	square kilometre	1,000,000 m sq	km sq
Volume	**Cubic Metre**	**SI Unit**	**m cu**
	cubic centimetre	0.000 001m cu	cm cu
Volume (fluids)	**Litre**	**0.001 m cu**	**1**
	millilitre	0.001 l	ml
	kilolitre	1,000 l (1m cu)	kl
Velocity	**Metre per Second**	**SI unit**	**m/s**
	kilometre per sec	0.27 m/s	km/h
	knot	1 n mile/h	kn or 0.514 m/s
Force	**Newton**	**SI Unit**	**N**
	kilonewton	1,000 N	kN
	meganewton	1,000 000 N	MN
Energy	**Joule**	**SI Unit**	**J**
	kilojoule	1,000 J	kJ
	megajoule	1,000 000 J	MJ
Power	**Watt**	**SI Unit**	**W**
	kilowatt	1,000W	kW
	megawatt	1,000 000W	MW

Density	**Kilogram per cubic Metre**	**SI Unit**	**Kg/m Cu metre**
	tonne per cubic metre	1,000 kg/m cu	t/m cu metre
	gram per cubic metre	0.001 kg/m cu	g/m cu metre
Density (fluids)	**Kilogram per litre**	**1,000 Kg/l**	**Kg/l**
Pressure	**Pascal**	**SI Unit (N/Msq)**	**Pa**
	kilopascal	1,000 Pa	kPa
	megapascal	1,000,000 Pa	MPa
	bar	100,000 Pa	bar
Electric Current	**Ampere**	**Base Unit**	**A**
	milliampere	0.001A	mA
Potential Difference	**Volt**	**SI Unit**	**V**
	microvolt	0.000 001V	µV
	millivolt	0.001V	mV
	kilovolt	1,000V	kV
	megavolt	1,000,000V	MV
Electrical	**Ohm**	**SI Unit**	Ω
Resistance	microhm	0.000 001	µΩ
	megohm	1,000,000	MΩ
Frequency	**Hertz**	**SI Unit**	**Hz**
	kilohertz	1,000 Hz	kHz
	megahertz	1,000,000 Hz	MHz
	gigahertz	1,000,000,000	GHz
Temperature	**Kelvin**	**SI Unit**	**K**
	degree Celsius	-273.15 K	C

Metric Units of Length

Metric Unit	Equivalent Value
1 metre	39.37 inches
	3.28083 feet
	1.09361 feet
	1000 millimetres
	100 centimetres
	10 decimetres
	0.001 kilometres
1 centimetre	0.3937 inch
	0.0328083 foot
	10 millimetres
	0.01 metres
1 millimetre	39.370 mils
	0.03937 inch
	0.001 metre
Kilometre	3280.83 feet
	1093.61 yards
	0.62137 mile
	1000 metres

US Units of Length

US Units	Equivalent Value
1 inch	1000 mils
	0.0833 foot
	0.0277 yard
	25.40 millimeters
	2.540 centimeters
1 foot	12 inches
	1.33333 yard
	0.0001893 miles
	0.30480 meter
	30.480 centimeters
1 yard	36 inches
	3 feet
	0.0005681 mile
	0.914402 meter
1 mile	63360 inches
	5280 feet
	1760 yards
	320 rods
	8 furlongs
	1609.35 meters
	1.60935 kilometers

Metric Units of Volume

Metric unit	Equivalent Value
1 cubic metre	61023.4 cubic inch
	35.3145 cubic feet
	1.30794 cubic yard
	1000 litres
1 cubic decimetre	61.0234 cubic inch
	0.035145 cubic foot
	1000 cubic centimetres
	1 litre
1 cubic centimetre	0.0000353 cubic foot
	0.0610234 cubic inch
	1000 cubic millimetres
	0.001 litre (1ml)
1 cubic millimetre	0.000061023 cubic inch
	0.0000000353 cubic foot
	0.001 cubic centimetre
1 litre	1 cubic decimetre
	61.0234 cubic inches
	0.351345 cubic foot
	1000 cubic centimetres
	0.001 cubic metre
	2.202 lbs of water

US Units of Volume

US Unit	Equivalent Value
1 cubic yard	46656 cubic inches
	27 cubic feet
	0.76456 cubic metre
1 cubic foot	1278 cubic inches
	0.03703703 cubic yard
	28.317 cubic decimetres
	0.028317 cubic meter
	7.4805 gallons
1 cubic inch	16.3872 cubic centimetres (16.3872 ml)
1 gallon (U.S.)	3.78543 litres
1 gallon (British)	4.54374 litres

Metric Units of Weight

Metric Unit	Equivalent Value
1 gram	15.432 grains 0.022046 lb 0.3527 oz.
1 kilogram	1000 grams 2.20462 lb 35.2739 oz.
1 metric ton	2204.62 pounds 0.984206 ton of 2240 pounds 22.0462 cwt 1.10231 ton of 2000 pounds 1000 kilograms

US Units of Weight

US Unit	Equivalent Value
1 ounce	437.5 grains 0.0625 pounds 28.3496 grams
1 pound	7000 grains 16 ounces 453.593 grams
1 ton (2000 pounds)	1.01605 metric tons 1016.05 kilograms

SI Prefixes

Prefix	Symbol	Value (words)	Value (numerical)
Giga	G	One thousand million	1,000,000,000
Mega	M	One million	1,000,000
Kilo	k	One thousand	1,000
Milli	m	One thousandth	0.001
Micro	u	One millionth	0.000,001
Nano	n	One thousand millionth	0.000,000,001

Metric to US Units

Quantity	Metric Unit	US Equivalent
Length	1 cm	0.394 in
	1 m	3.28 ft
	1 m	1.09 yd
	1 km	0.621 mile
Mass	1 g	0.0353 oz
	1 kg	2.20 lb
	1 tonne	0.984 ton
Area	1 cm sq	0.155 in sq
	1 m sq	10.8 ft sq
	1 m sq	1.20 yd sq
	1 ha	2.47 ac
	1 km sq	247 ac
Volume	1 cm cu	0.0610 in cu
	1 m cu	35.3 ft cu
	1 m cu	1.31 yd cu
	1 m cu	27.5 bushels

Quantity	Metric Unit	US Equivalent
Volume (fluids)	1 ml	0.0352 fl oz
	1 litre	1.76 pint
	1 m cu	220 gallons
Force	1N (newton)	0.225 lbf
Pressure	1 kPa	0.145 psi
Velocity	1 km/h	0.621 mph
Temperature	°C	$\frac{9 \times {}^{0}C}{5} + 32°F$
Energy	1 kJ	0.948 Btu joule
Power	1 kW	1.34 hp

US to Metric Units

Quantity	Metric Unit	US Equivalent
Length	1 in	25.4 mm
	1 ft	30.5 cm
	1 yd	0.914 m
	1 mile	1.61 km
Mass	1 oz	28.3 g
	1 lb	454 g
	1 ton	1.02 tonne
Area	1 in sq	6.45 cm sq
	1 ft sq	929 cm sq
	1 yd sq	0.836 m sq
	1 ac sq	0.405 ha
	1 sq mile	259 ha
Volume	1 in cu	16.4 cm cu
	1 ft cu	0.02383 m cu
	1 yd cu	0.765 m cu
	1 bushel	0.0364 m cu
Volume (fluids)	1 fl oz	28.4 ml
	1 pint	568 ml
	1 gallon (US)	3.79 litre
Force	1 lbf (pound force)	4.45 N
Pressure	1 psi (lb/sq in)	6.89 kPa
Velocity	1 mph	1.61 km/h
Temperature	°F	$\frac{5}{9}$ (f - 32)°C
Energy	1 Btu	1.06 kJ thermal unit
Power	1 hp	0.746 kW

Fraction	Decimal (mm)	Decimal (in)
1/16	1.58750	0.0625
1/8	3.17501	0.125
3/16	4.76251	0.1875
1/4	6.35001	0.2500
5/16	7.93752	0.3125
3/8	9.52502	0.3750
7/16	11.11252	0.4375
1/2	12.70003	0.5000
9/16	14.28753	0.5625
5/8	15.87503	0.625
11/16	17.46253	0.6875
3/4	19.05004	0.75000
13/16	20.63754	0.8125
7/8	22.22504	0.8750
15/16	23.81255	0.9375

Celsius to Fahrenheit

Celsius (°C)	Fahrenheit (°F)
-9	15.8
-8	17.6
-7	19.4
-6	21.2
-5	23
-4	24.8
-3	26.6
-2	28.4
-1	30.2
0	32
5	41
10	50
15	59
20	68
25	77
30	86
35	95
40	104
45	113
50	122

Glossary

Absolute Pressure - Pressure measured from absolute zero

Absolute temperature - Temperature measured above absolute zero.

Actuators - e.g. a lever, solenoid etc on a valve, cylinder or motor.

Adiabatic expansion - The expansion or compression of a gas without change in heat content.

Aftercooler - Aftercoolers are generally placed after the compressor to deliberately cool the air and remove some of the water from the air before that air enters the system.

Air motors - Rotary motion can be produced by air motors. They can be very large and robust or very small. Speeds of up to 20,000 revolutions per minute can be achieved by such motors.

Air power - Compressed air has properties which allow force to be transmitted and multiplied. It is compressible and pressure is distributed throughout the enclosed system so that power can be converted to mechanical power doing useful work.

Air preparation - The removal of contaminants by cooling and filtering. The reducing of pressure by regulators and the adding of oil to the air with lubricators.

Air receiver - A pressure vessel for storing energy in a pneumatic system in the form of compressed air.

Ambient temperature - Temperature of the environment

Atmospheric pressure - The absolute pressure of the atmosphere as measured for a given altitude

Axial piston compressor - In the axial piston compressor, the pistons move parallel to the rotating shaft.

Bar - An International unit of pressure (ISO Standards)

Bi-directional - Bi-directional motors rotate in both directions.

Braiding - An intermeshing network of wire covered by rubber. This gives strength to the pneumatic hose.

Bypass - A non-return valve allowing air to bypass another valve in one direction only.

Capacity (compressor) - Actual volume rate of flow, compressed and delivered at the discharge point, at stated inlet conditions.

Check valve - Check valves block the flow of air in a given direction and allow the free flow of air in the opposite direction.

Compression ratio - Ratio of final pressure to original pressure.

Compressor - Industrial pneumatic systems are generally powered by compressors, which in turn, are driven by electricity.

Compressor regulator - A device, fitted to a compressor which controls the output of the machine.

Condensate - Liquid formed by the condensation of water vapor in the air, due to a fall in temperature.

Contamination - The presence of any substance in a pneumatic system that is detrimental to that system.

Control chamber - Air from the main line passes through a narrow channel into the chamber above the poppet in a relief valve This is called the control chamber.

Cracking pressure - If the system pressure reaches a preset value, or cracking pressure, air will flow.

Detent - Retains the position of a control mechanism in directional control valves. For example, if the valve is activated by a pedal the detent prevents the valve moving back to its original position when the pressure on the pedal is removed.

Diaphragm compressor - This compressor works on the same principle as the piston compressor but the piston is separated from the suction chamber by a **diaphragm**.

Differential cylinders - These have different size areas at each side of the cylinder piston as the piston rod reduces one area. Hence these cylinders are referred to as differential type cylinders.

Directional control valves - Place at the right time. We achieve this by incorporating directional control valves into the system. These direct the flow of air into the correct pipelines.

Discharge temperature - Temperature at the standard discharge point of a compressor.

Displacement - The volume displaced by the compression element in a given time.

Double acting cylinder - If a cylinder both extends and retracts due to air flow and pressure, it is a double acting cylinder.

Dryer - A dryer can sometimes be placed before the air receiver. This helps prevent condensation in the receiver and any subsequent corrosion.

Electrical solenoid valves - Valves which open or close under electromagnetic control to release, restrict or stop the flow of air

Exhaust port - The outlet for air which has done work. This is vented to the atmosphere.

Fan cooler - A fan cooler is like the type used in a motor car engine. Air flows through the cooler as a fan blows cool air across the surface of the cooler.

Filter - A device whose primary function is the retention by a porous medium of insoluble contaminant from compressed air.

Flexible pipe work - Flexible hosing is used not only because it allows actuators greater freedom of movement. It also can dampen down any noise that may be transmitted through the system. In particular it can control the vibration effects from compressors and pneumatic motors.

Flow control valves - These are used widely in pneumatic systems to slow down actuators when lower velocities are required. They do this by controlling the rate of flow of air from one part of the circuit to another.

Flowmeter - Gauge which measures flow volume rate i.e Litres/second

Fluids - Substances (both liquids and gases) that change shape easily and take on the form of their containers. This makes it possible for fluids to pass through the openings of different shapes and sizes within the components of a fluid power system.

Force - That which changes the direction or speed of the motion of a fluid or body. It is measured in Newtons or pounds.

Force multiplication - A pneumatic system can not only transmit forces but can multiply those forces. This means that very large loads can be handled using a relatively low force input.

Fusible plug - Fitted to the hot discharge zone of a compressor for thermal protection

Gauge pressure - Pressure measured above or below atmospheric pressure

Intercooling - The cooling of compressed air between compression stages.

Isothermal expansion - Expansion or compression without change of temperature

Imperial units - Standards legally established in Great Britain e.g., feet, gallons, pounds, inches, horsepower etc.

Inertia - The inherent property of matter by which it tends to remain at rest when still and in motion when moving

Intake filters - An air intake filter is connected to the air inlet port of the compressor to prevent solid contaminants entering the compression chamber of the compressor.

ISO - International Standards Organization.

Leakage - Loss of air to the atmosphere due to faulty valves, fittings etc.

Linear actuator - A cylinder which produces linear motion would be an example of a linear actuator. It converts gas pressure into mechanical force or motion.

Load - The mass that the system is maneuvering by means of mechanical force or motion.

Lubricator - Most pneumatic system equipment requires lubricator to reduce friction on moving parts and to give a longer working life. The most common type of lubricator is the 'oil mist' lubricator where the oil is discharged directly into the air line as a fine mist or fog.

Main pressure control valve - Most pneumatic circuits have a main pressure control valve. This sets the maximum working pressure in the system.

Multi-stage compressor - Two or more stages of compression, with intercooling between them, before the final pressure is reached.

Nomogram - It is essential that the proper diameter pipe is inserted into the different parts of a pneumatic system. You must be certain that a given diameter of pipe will move a volume of air down the system at the required flow rate. To help us calculate this, we use a nomogram.

Non differential cylinders - Where two piston rods are incorporated into the construction, the area available for air to work on is the same. Hence these are non-differential cylinders. Same area on both sides of the piston.

Non-variable restrictors - The simplest method of flow control is to insert a restrictor, i.e pipework of a smaller diameter. However this restriction is non variable, providing only a fixed reduction in flow.

Normally closed valve (Non passing) - A valve that blocks flow between ports.

Normally open valve (Passing) - A valve that does not restrict flow.

Orifice - A restriction, the length of which is relatively small with respect to its cross-sectional area.

Overall stage ratio - The pressure ratio for any particular pressure stage in a multi-stage compressor.

Pascal - Blaise Pascal, a 17th century French mathematician who studied the properties of liquids.

Pascal's law - 'Pascal's Law' states that "pressure exerted on a confined fluid is transmitted undiminished in all directions and acts with equal force on **all equal** areas"

Pilot line - This device senses pressure from a given part of a circuit.

Pilot operated - Utilizes a signal, spotting a change in pressure, to actuate a valve.

Pilot operated spool valve - A directional control valve which is operated by using pilot pressure from another part of the circuit.

Piston compressor - The compression of air by means of a piston or piston moving in a chamber.

Pneumatic cylinder - A device for producing linear movement from air flow and pressure.

Pneumatic pressure - Force per unit area measured in Bar or Newtons per centimetre squared.

Pneumatic symbols - These represent components in circuit diagrams. The standards are international, laid down by the International Standards Organization (ISO).

Pneumatics - The use of gases as power systems. This transmission of power through gases can be converted to mechanical power.

Poppet - A device fitted to a seat which gives good sealing characteristics. Any increase in system pressure above the poppet tends to decrease the leakage between the poppet and the seat. It also increases the force holding the poppet against the seat, ensuring a tighter seal.

Poppet relief valve - A type of simple relief valve which has a poppet acting as a seal rather than a spool. This type of valve is used on an air receiver to protect the system from pressure overload.

Port - Point at which air enters or leaves a valve or other pneumatic component.

Pressure control valves - By controlling the system pressure we can limit the forces applied to the actuators and avoid any undue stresses on the machinery. We achieve this control by incorporating pressure control valves into our circuit design.

Pressure gauge - A device for measuring the pressure of compressed air.

Pressure ratio (total) - The ratio between the absolute discharge pressure and the absolute inlet pressure.

Pressure regulating valve (Pressure reducing valve) - This acts to lower the pressure in a secondary circuit, thereby lowering the force or torque acting on an actuator.

Pressure reducing valve - A valve used to limit the maximum system pressure, exhausting the compressed air to atmosphere when the safe working pressure is exceeded.

psi - An imperial unit of pressure - Pounds per square inch.

Pulsation damper - A vessel fitted at the discharge of a reciprocating compressor to remove pulsations and to prevent resonance.

Reciprocating compressor - The reciprocating or piston compressor is widely used in industry and can be a single stage or multi-stage type.

Relief valves - Relief valves set the working pressure within a pneumatic system. They can be considered as safety valves.

Resistance - Opposition to the passage of a fluid through a pneumatic system due to friction, drag and restrictions.

Restrictor - A device which restricts the flow of air in a circuit.

Rigid pipe work - In all pneumatic systems, the compressor, valves and actuators are connected together by pipes. Rigid pipe work is manufactured to high standards. It is used primarily for the main and branch lines and is made of galvanized steel.

Ring main - A compressed air main which begins and ends at the compressor providing every outlet with two possible directions of supply.

Rod - A metal rod which transmits force to and from the piston and the load.

Roots blower - These are very simple constructions. They can generate a pressure of up to 3 bar (43.5 psi). Air passes through the unit without a change in volume but the delivery pressure relies on the back pressure of the system since no compression takes place in the compressor.

Rotary compressor - The rotary compressor, also called a **vane** compressor, has a rotor mounted eccentrically in the compression chamber. They are highly efficient but have pressure limitation of approximately 10 bar (145psi).

Rotary screw compressor - The rotary screw compressor is designed with two intermeshing rotors with helical lobes. Pressures up to10 bar(145psi) plus high flow rates are achieved by these very quiet compressors.

Seal - A device that prevents or controls the escape of air or the entry of a foreign material.

Sequence valve - These valves control the flow of air between different parts of the circuit allowing actuators to operate in sequence. These valves are normally closed (non passing). And similar to a relief valve in operation.

Separator - A device for removing liquids from compressed air.

Shock - A sudden force on an actuator.

Single acting cylinder - If a cylinder extends due to air pressure and flow and retracts due to another force such as a spring or gravity, it is single acting.

Single stage compression - Initial to final pressure in a single step.

Speed - The distance travelled per unit of time.

Spool - A device which moves in a linear direction to vary the direction of air flow.

Stroke - An extension or retraction in one direction of a piston within a cylinder.

Symbol - These represent components in circuit diagrams. The standards are international, laid down by the International Standards Organisation (ISO).

Telescopic cylinder - Where cylinders are nested one within the other to provide a long extension they are described as telescopic cylinders.

Temperature - A measure of heat in either degrees Celsius or Fahrenheit.

Torque - The force generated by rotary motion is called torque. It is measured in Nm, Newton metres or pound-inches.

Unidirectional motors - Unidirectional motors rotate in a single direction.

Valve - A device that controls air flow, direction, pressure or flow rate.

2/2 valve - The first number in the 2/2 designation refers to the number of ports in the valve. Thus a 2/2 valve has two working ports, an 'in' and an 'out' port. The second number in the designation refers to the number of positions the valve can take. In this case, it is two.

3/2 valve - The first number in the 3/2 designation refers to the number of ports in the valve. Thus a 3/2 valve has three working ports. The second number in the designation refers to the number of positions the valve can take. In this case, it is two.

4/2 valve - The first number in the 4/2 designation refers to the number of ports in the valve. Thus a 4/2 valve has four working ports. The second number in the designation refers to the number of positions the valve can take. In this case, it is two.

4/3 valve - The first number in the 4/3 designation refers to the number of ports in the valve. Thus a 4/3 valve has four working ports. The second number in the designation refers to the number of positions the valve can take. In this case, it is three.

5/2 valve - The first number in the 5/2 designation refers to the number of ports in the valve. Thus a 5/2 valve has five working ports. The second number in the designation refers to the number of positions the valve can take. In this case, it is two.

5/3 valve - The first number in the 5/3 designation refers to the number of ports in the valve. Thus 5/3 valve has five working ports. The second number in the designation refers to the number of positions the valve can take. In this case, it is three.

Valve actuator - All valves require some form of actuator to move the spool to each working position. These range from spring actuators, which ensure the valve always returns to the correct initial position, to electrical solenoid valves that can operate from sophisticated electronic control systems on fully automatic machines.

Variable restrictor - Here the level of restriction can be altered. This is done, for example, by turning the screw head to open or close the channel. This alters the flow rate through the valve.

Volume - The cubic or content measured in cubic metres.

Volumetric efficiency - Ratio of capacity to displacement of a compressor or vacuum pump.

Water cooler - With water coolers, air and water flow through the unit down two separate pipe networks. These two networks are linked by heat conducting pipes or fins to transfer the heat from the air to the water. By cooling compressor air, water is condensed out which could reduce the life of components.

Work - The act of producing an effect by means of a force (F) whose point of application moves through a distance (d) in its own line of action, measured by the product of the force and the distance (W=Fd).

Working pressure - The maximum pressure which the system is designed to operate under.